BTEC Level 2 First Study Skills Guide in Applied Science

Welcome to your Study Skills Guide! You can make it your own – start by adding your personal and course details below...

Learner's name: _____

BTEC course title: _____

Date started: _____

Mandatory units:

_____

_____

_____

Optional units:

_____

_____

_____

Centre name: _____

Centre address:

_____

_____

_____

Tutor's name: _____

Published by Pearson Education Limited, a company incorporated in England and Wales, having its registered office at Edinburgh Gate, Harlow, Essex, CM20 2JE. Registered company number: 872828

Edexcel is a registered trademark of Edexcel Limited

Text © Pearson Education Limited 2010

First published 2010

16 15 14
26 25 24

British Library Cataloguing in Publication Data
A catalogue record for this book is available from the British Library

ISBN 978 1 84690 579 7

Typeset and edited by Ken Vail Graphic Design
Cover design by Visual Philosophy, created by EMC Design
Cover photo/illustration © Science Photo Library Ltd: Tek Image
Printed and bound by L.E.G.O. S.p.A. Lavis (TN) - Italy

Acknowledgements
The author and publisher would like to thank the following individuals and organisations for permission to reproduce photographs:
Alamy Images: Jeff Greenberg 48, Ace Stock Limited 54; **Corbis:** 62, Comstock 5, Lester Lefkowitz 40; **iStockphoto:** Murat Giray Kaya 83, Oman Mirzaie 83/2, Ales Veluscek 79; **Pearson Education Ltd:** Steve Shott 22, Ian Wedgewood 33; **Photolibrary.com:** Pixtal Images 36; **TopFoto:** John Powell 18
Cover images: *Front:* **Science Photo Library Ltd:** TEK IMAGE
All other images © Pearson Education

Every effort has been made to contact copyright holders of material reproduced in this book. Any omissions will be rectified in subsequent printings if notice is given to the publishers.

Websites
Go to www.pearsonhotlinks.co.uk to gain access to the relevant website links and information on how they can aid your studies. When you access the site, search for either the express code 5797S, title BTEC Level 2 First Study Skills Guide in Applied Science or ISBN 9781846905797.

Disclaimer
This material has been published on behalf of Edexcel and offers high-quality support for the delivery of Edexcel qualifications.
This does not mean that the material is essential to achieve any Edexcel qualification, nor does it mean that it is the only suitable material available to support any Edexcel qualification. Edexcel material will not be used verbatim in setting any Edexcel examination or assessment. Any resource lists produced by Edexcel shall include this and other appropriate resources. Copies of official specifications for all Edexcel qualifications may be found on the Edexcel website: www.edexcel.com

Contents

Your BTEC First course 5
   Early days 5
   About your course 6
   Introduction to the applied science sector 11
   More about BTEC Level 2 Firsts 14

Getting the most from your BTEC 15
   Knowing yourself 15
   Managing your time 21
   Getting the most from work experience 25
   Getting experience of work in applied science 27
   Working with other people 31
   Getting the most from special events 36

Resources and research 39
   Understanding resources 39
   Finding the information you need 43
   Keeping a logbook 49

Managing your information 51
   Organising and selecting your information 51
   Interpreting and presenting your information 53
   Making presentations 62

Your assessments 65
   The importance of assignments 65
   Coping with problems 87

Skills building 89
   Personal, learning and thinking skills (PLTS) 89
   Functional skills 90

Answers 97
   Skills building answers 97

Accessing website links 98

Useful terms 99

Popular progression pathways

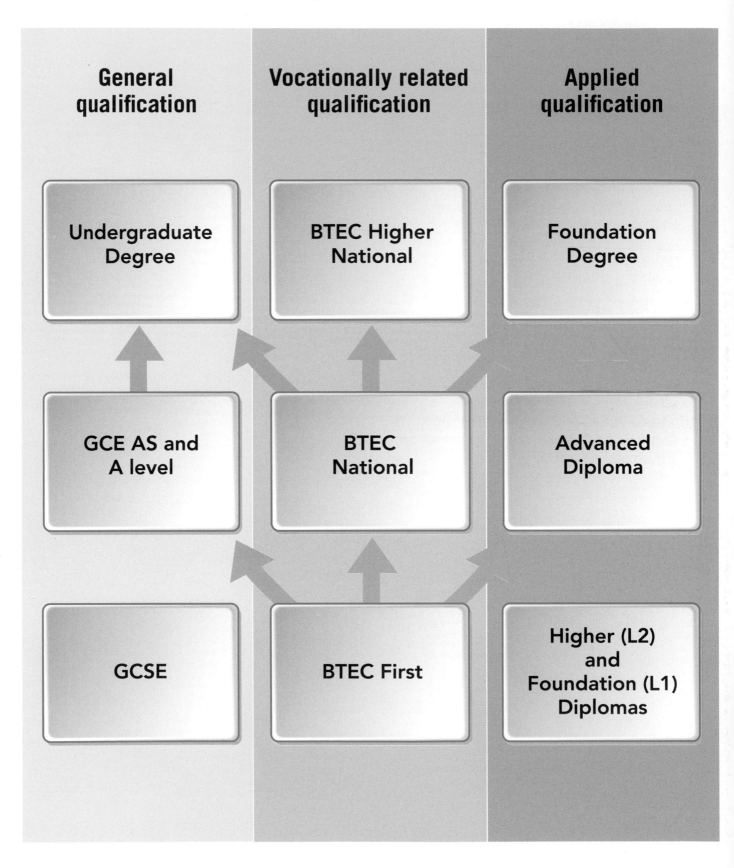

Your BTEC First course
Early days

Every year many new learners start BTEC Level 2 First courses, enjoy the challenge and successfully achieve their award. Some do this the easy way; others make it harder for themselves.

Everyone will have different feelings when they start their course.

Case study: Thinking positively

Sadaf and Liam are taking the BTEC First in Applied Science. They are very different people with contrasting attitudes. Some of their characteristics are set out below.

Sadaf is a very hard-working girl and her dream is to go to university to study to become a midwife. However, at the moment, she is finding that her English holds her back and some of the Applied Science course is difficult to understand. Sadaf tries to maintain a positive approach – she always asks her tutor for help when she is struggling, listens to the advice given and acts to improve her work to get the best possible grades. She also reads science books in her spare time to help with her understanding of science and improve her English.

Liam has a more negative outlook. He doesn't really know what he wants to do with his life and does not have a good track record in education. He is often rude to his tutors and peers, and refuses any help offered to him. He loves to listen to his MP3 player and gets annoyed when he is asked to stop this in lessons. However, he has always managed to pass his exams and coursework with the bare minimum of effort. Liam is naturally quite talented in science subjects and particularly likes practical activities. He doesn't agree with homework and avoids it like the plague, choosing to hang out with his friends instead. This has got him into trouble on numerous occasions as his coursework is often late.

Sadaf may sometimes struggle with her studies but she is not letting this get to her and has decided to think positively. How do you think Sadaf's can-do attitude will help her as she works toward her goal of becoming a midwife?

Liam is managing to complete his BTEC coursework but his attitude has already got him into trouble several times. Do you think Liam's negative approach will lead to further problems in the future? What kind of things might happen? If Liam decided to think positively about his studies, like Sadaf, how could he prevent these problems?

About your course

What do you know already?

If someone asks you about your course, could you give a short, accurate description? If you can, you have a good understanding of what your course is about. This has several benefits.

Four benefits of understanding your course
1 You will be better prepared and organised.
2 You can make links between the course and the world around you.
3 You can check how your personal interests and hobbies relate to the course.
4 You will be alert to information that relates to topics you are studying, whether it's from conversations with family and friends, watching television or at a part-time job.

Read any information you have been given by your centre. You can also check the Edexcel website for further details – go to www.edexcel.com.

Interest/hobby	How this relates to my studies

What else do you need to know?

Five facts you should find out about your course

1. The type of BTEC qualification you are studying.
2. How many credits your qualification is worth.
3. The number of mandatory units you will study and what they cover.
4. How many credits the mandatory units are worth.
5. The number of optional units you need to study in total and the options available in your centre.

Case study: Applying science knowledge and skills

Faith has been a gymnast for the past 10 years and now represents her county in the sport. She has a part-time job coaching the younger gymnasts. Faith wants to create a booklet that will help the young gymnasts learn about the anatomy of their bodies. The booklet will also give examples of exercises to improve a gymnast's fitness and will introduce some of the physics behind different moves on the beam, bars, vault and floor.

Faith is a very good example of someone who has used her interests and part-time work to help to develop her science skills. She will be able to use this when she applies for jobs.

Employers like the fact that interviewees can apply their knowledge and understanding of the course to everyday life, especially in a business-like context, such as sport or part-time work.

Think about any of your part-time jobs, voluntary work, or interests that give you the opportunity to apply your knowledge of science, or to gain other valuable skills. How do these activities allow you to use your knowledge of science in a real-life context? If you don't currently have an opportunity to apply your knowledge of science, think of part-time jobs, voluntary work or hobbies that you could take up to do this.

BTEC FACT

BTEC First Certificate = 15 credits

BTEC First Extended Certificate = 30 credits

BTEC First Diploma = 60 credits

Generally, the more credits there are, the longer it takes to study for the qualification.

TRY THIS

Find out which optional units your centre offers. To check the topics covered in each unit go to www.pearsonhotlinks.co.uk, insert the express code 5797S and click on the link for this page.

TOP TIP

If you have a choice of optional units in your centre and are struggling to decide, talk through your ideas with your tutor.

Activity: How well do you know your course?

Complete this activity to check that you know the main facts. Compare your answers with a friend. You should have similar answers except where you make personal choices, such as about optional units. Your tutor can help you complete number 9.

1 The correct title of the BTEC award I am studying is:

_____

_____

2 The length of time it will take me to complete my award is:

_____

_____

3 The number of mandatory units I have to study is:

_____

_____

4 The titles of my mandatory units, and their credit values, are:

_____

_____

_____

_____

_____

_____

_____

_____

_____

_____

5 The main topics I will learn in each mandatory unit include:

Mandatory unit	Main topics

6 The number of credits I need to achieve by studying optional units is:

7 The titles of my optional units, and their credit values, are:

8 The main topics I will learn in each optional unit include:

Optional unit	Main topics

9 Other important aspects of my course are:

10 After I have achieved my BTEC First, my options include:

Introduction to the applied science sector

The BTEC First in Applied Science provides learners with the skills and knowledge that underpin all aspects of science in a work-related context. Following the course could help you succeed in your chosen career or to access higher education. You could achieve the necessary grades to go on to study science at Level 3, for example a BTEC National qualification in forensic or medical science. In some centres, you might be accepted for AS-level courses in biology, chemistry or physics. Later, you could gain a place at university to study for a degree in one of a wide range of science-related subjects, such as chemical engineering, biomedical science, human physiology or astrophysics.

As well as knowledge and skills, this course also provides you with work-related experience which is invaluable for any science-based job, for example in the health professions, pharmaceutical industries, research or environmental agencies.

The BTEC First Applied Science course covers all aspects of science, including biology, chemistry, and physics, as well as maths and health and safety-related issues. You will complete assignments based on scientific job-related scenarios, for example working as a science technician, producing information for the public and conducting scientific research. As well as exploring a range of scientific concepts, you will use your IT skills to produce documents for assessment. Other skills you will practise include researching, preparing and giving presentations, producing scientific reports, following instructions for practical investigations and effective time management.

Case study: Introduction to your sector

Lauren is very interested in becoming a science technician. She is taking the following units in her BTEC First in Applied Science course:

- Unit 1 Chemistry and Our Earth
- Unit 2 Energy and Our Universe
- Unit 3 Biology and Our Environment
- Unit 6 Health Applications of Life Science
- Unit 7 Scientific Practical Project
- Unit 16 Designing and Making Useful Devices Using Science

What kinds of things do you think Lauren will learn that will help her in her role as a science technician? Think about what you would like to do when you complete the course. How will the units you have chosen help in your future career?

Skills you need for your sector

You will be expected to use some or all of the following skills when completing assignments for your BTEC First in Applied Science:

- IT skills
- selecting information
- problem solving
- following procedures and processes
- implementing health and safety procedures
- keeping your notes in good order for ease of reference
- presenting work
- referencing work
- English and maths skills.

Activity: Skills required for jobs in your sector

How good are you at the skills shown in the list on page 11? Use two different highlighter pens to identify those that you are good at and those that require further practice.

Now think about IT skills. Complete the following table to say how these IT skills could be useful in a science-related job.

IT skill	Example of science-related job	Why is this an essential skill for the job?
internet-researching skills	research scientist looking into a cure for diabetes	
saving files	chemical engineer working on a new product	
retrieving files	science technician	
security	working for the NHS inputting patient data following analysis of blood samples	
emailing	promotion officer for the National Space Centre	
producing PowerPoint presentations	public liaison officer for an environmental agency	
Using Publisher, Excel and Word packages effectively	writer for a scientific magazine	

Have a go at the following activity to improve your skills in IT and selecting information. Use the internet to research three scientific things you are interested in and write a paragraph in your own words on each topic.

Topic 1

_____

_____

_____

_____

Topic 2

_____

_____

_____

_____

Topic 3

_____

_____

_____

_____

You can find more help with some of these skills on pages 53–64 in the section on Interpreting and Presenting your Information.

More about BTEC Level 2 Firsts

What is different about a BTEC Level 2 First?

How you learn

Expect to be 'hands-on'. BTEC Level 2 Firsts are practical and focus on the skills and knowledge needed in the workplace. You will learn new things and learn how to apply your knowledge.

BTEC First learners are expected to take responsibility for their own learning and to be keen and well-organised. You should enjoy having more freedom, while knowing you can still ask for help or support if you need it.

How you are assessed

Many BTEC First courses are completed in one year, but if you are taking GCSEs as well you may be doing it over two years or more. You will be assessed by completing **assignments** written by your tutors. These are based on **learning outcomes** set by Edexcel. Each assignment will have a deadline.

TOP TIP

You can use your Study Skills Guide with the Edexcel Student Book for BTEC Level 2 First Applied Science (Edexcel, 2010). It includes the main knowledge you'll need, with tips from BTEC experts, Edexcel assignment tips, assessment activities and up-to-date case studies from industry experts, plus handy references to your Study Skills Guide.

BTEC FACT

On a BTEC course you achieve individual criteria at pass, merit or distinction for your assignments. You will receive a pass, merit or distinction **grade** for completed units and then one of these three grades for the whole course.

Case study: Working independently

Alison hasn't studied a BTEC course before and she has already found out that they are different from GCSE courses.

After a few BTEC lessons, Alison has realised that she needs to be more independent and responsible in her approach to assignments and that it is up to her to find the motivation to get things done. This is a big change for her; previously she would have been given work by her teacher and told exactly what to do.

Alison has been thinking about how she needs to change in order to be more effective at working independently, so that she can use the information given to her by her tutors, along with each assignment brief, to complete her assignments for the deadlines.

How independent are you? Think about the ways in which you have worked independently before.

How good are you at managing your time? You could try using a diary to plan for the next two weeks, including assignment work, home, social and job-related commitments.

Getting the most from your BTEC

Getting the most from your BTEC involves several skills, such as using your time effectively and working well with other people. Knowing yourself is also important.

Knowing yourself

How would you describe yourself? Make some notes here.

_____

_____

_____

_____

_____

_____

_____

_____

_____

If you described yourself to someone else, would you be able to sum up your temperament and personality, identify your strengths and weaknesses and list your skills? If not, is it because you've never thought about it or because you honestly don't have a clue?

Learning about yourself is often called self-analysis. You may have already done personality tests or careers profiles. If not, there are many available online. However, the information you gain from these profiles is useless unless you can apply it to what you are doing.

Your personality

Everyone is different. For example, some people:

- like to plan in advance; others prefer to be spontaneous
- love being part of a group; others prefer one or two close friends
- enjoy being the life and soul of the party; others prefer to sit quietly and they feel uncomfortable at large social gatherings
- are imaginative and creative; others prefer to deal only with facts
- think carefully about all their options before making a decision; others follow their 'gut instincts' and often let their heart rule their head.

Case study: Your personality and the BTEC First

Jane and Mohamed are both studying the BTEC First in Applied Science.

Jane is very quiet and hard working. She prefers to work alone, but can work with others if she has to. She is very creative, loves biology and wants to pursue a career in science.

Mohamed is loud and outgoing. He is very friendly and loves to work with other people. He enjoys practical work, especially chemistry investigations, and is very intelligent. However, he often needs guidance to complete his work as he is easily distracted.

Think about whether you are more like Jane or Mohamed. Which of the following jobs do you think you would be most suited to and why:

- research scientist working on a cure for cancer
- supervisor of a drugs trial with a pharmaceutical company
- chemical engineer working for a large company
- science technician working in a college?

You may need to carry out some research into exactly what each job entails.

TRY THIS

Imagine one of your friends is describing your best features. What would they say?

Personalities in the workplace

There's a mix of personalities in most workplaces. Some people prefer to work behind the scenes, such as many IT practitioners, who like to concentrate on tasks they enjoy doing. Others love high-profile jobs, where they may often be involved in high-pressure situations, such as paramedics and television presenters. Most people fall somewhere between these two extremes.

In any job there will be some aspects that are more appealing and interesting than others. If you have a part-time job you will already know this. The same thing applies to any course you take!

Your personality and your BTEC First course

Understanding your personality means you can identify which parts of your course you are likely to find easy and which more difficult. Working out the aspects you need to develop should be positive. You can also think about how your strengths and weaknesses may affect other people.

- Natural planners find it easier to schedule work for assignments.
- Extroverts like giving presentations and working with others but may overwhelm quieter team members.
- Introverts often prefer to work alone and may be excellent at researching information.

Activity: What is your personality type?

1a) Identify your own personality type, either by referring to a personality test you have done recently or by going online and doing a reliable test. Go to www.pearsonhotlinks.co.uk, insert the express code 5797S and click on the link for this activity.

Print a summary of the completed test or write a brief description of the results for future reference.

b) Use this information to identify the tasks and personal characteristics that you find easy or difficult.

	Easy	Difficult
Being punctual		
Planning how to do a job		
Working neatly and accurately		
Being well organised		
Having good ideas		
Taking on new challenges		
Being observant		
Working with details		
Being patient		
Coping with criticism		
Dealing with customers		
Making decisions		
Keeping calm under stress		
Using your own initiative		

	Easy	Difficult
Researching facts carefully and accurately		
Solving problems		
Meeting deadlines		
Finding and correcting your errors		
Clearing up after yourself		
Helping other people		
Working as a member of a team		
Being sensitive to the needs of others		
Respecting other people's opinions		
Being tactful and discreet		
Being even-tempered		

2 Which thing from your 'difficult' list do you think you should work on improving first? Start by identifying the benefits you will gain. Then decide how to achieve your goal.

> **BTEC FACT**
>
> All BTEC First courses enable you to develop your personal, learning and thinking skills (**PLTS**), which will help you to meet new challenges more easily. (See page 89.)

Your knowledge and skills

You already have a great deal of knowledge, as well as practical and personal skills gained at school, at home and at work (if you have a part-time job). Now you need to assess these to identify your strengths and weaknesses.

To do this accurately, try to identify evidence for your knowledge and skills. Obvious examples are:

- previous qualifications
- school reports
- occasions when you have demonstrated particular skills, such as communicating with customers or colleagues in a part-time job.

TOP TIP

The more you understand your own personality, the easier it is to build on your strengths and compensate for your weaknesses.

Part-time jobs give you knowledge and skills in a real work setting.

Activity: Check your skills

1 Score yourself from 1 to 5 for each of the skills in the table on the next two pages.

  1 = I'm very good at this skill.

  2 = I'm good but could improve this skill.

  3 = This skill is only average and I know that I need to improve it.

  4 = I'm weak at this skill and must work hard to improve it.

  5 = I've never had the chance to develop this skill.

  Enter the score in the column headed 'Score A' and add today's date.

2 Look back at the units and topics you will be studying for your course – you entered them into the chart on page 9. Use this to identify any additional skills that you know are important for your course and add them to the table. Then score yourself for these skills, too.

3 Identify the main skills you will need in order to be successful in your chosen career, and highlight them in the table.

  Go back and score yourself against each skill after three, six and nine months. That way you can monitor your progress and check where you need to take action to develop the most important skills you will need.

English and communication skills	Score A (today) Date:	Score B (after three months) Date:	Score C (after six months) Date:	Score D (after nine months) Date:
Reading and understanding different types of texts and information				
Speaking to other people face to face				
Speaking clearly on the telephone				
Listening carefully				
Writing clearly and concisely				
Presenting information in a logical order				
Summarising information				
Using correct punctuation and spelling				
Joining in a group discussion				
Expressing your own ideas and opinions appropriately				
Persuading other people to do something				
Making an oral presentation and presenting ideas clearly				
ICT skills	Score A (today) Date:	Score B (after three months) Date:	Score C (after six months) Date:	Score D (after nine months) Date:
Using ICT equipment correctly and safely				
Using a range of software				
Accurate keyboarding				
Proofreading				
Using the internet to find and select appropriate information				
Using ICT equipment to communicate and exchange information				
Producing professional documents which include tables and graphics				
Creating and interpreting spreadsheets				
Using PowerPoint				

Maths and numeracy skills	Score A (today) Date:	Score B (after three months) Date:	Score C (after six months) Date:	Score D (after nine months) Date:
Carrying out calculations (eg money, time, measurements, etc) in a work-related situation				
Estimating amounts				
Understanding and interpreting data in tables, graphs, diagrams and charts				
Comparing prices and identifying best value for money				
Solving routine and non-routine work-related numerical problems				

Case study: Previous skills and experience

Olivia wants to go to university to become a school science teacher or a science tutor in a college. She is a good learner who works very hard and loves science. However, she gets extremely nervous when it comes to exams, so has decided to do the BTEC First in Applied Science, which uses assignments for assessment, instead of GCSEs with their all-important exams.

Olivia wants to feel really well prepared so that she succeeds on this course to the best of her abilities. She decides to make a list of the knowledge and skills from previous studies that will help her to pass the course. This will make her feel more confident in her abilities.

Here is her list.

Knowledge I have from my previous studies	Skills I have from my previous studies
KS3 Biology	working safely in experiment
KS3 Physics	using laboratory equipment safely
KS3 Chemistry	planning investigations
KS3 Maths	performing investigations
KS3 English	evaluating investigations
KS3 Information Technology	producing graphs and tables from data, working in groups, presenting a poster to my classmates, essay writing, using computers to research information, present data and prepare presentations

Think about the BTEC First in Applied Science course and make your own list of relevant knowledge and skills gathered previously in your studies. You will feel more confident when you identify the range of attributes that you **already** have to help you complete this course. You will probably have more science knowledge and skills than you realised!

Managing your time

Some people are brilliant at managing their time. They do everything they need to and have time left over for activities they enjoy. Other people complain that they don't know where the time goes.

Which are you? If you need help to manage your time – and most people do – you will find help here.

Why time management is important

- It means you stay in control, get less stressed and don't skip important tasks.
- Some weeks will be peaceful, others will be hectic.
- The amount of homework and assignments you have to do will vary.
- As deadlines approach, time always seems to go faster.
- Some work will need to be done quickly, maybe for the next lesson; other tasks may need to be done over several days or weeks. This needs careful planning.
- You may have several assignments or tasks to complete in a short space of time.
- You want to have a social life.

Avoiding time-wasting

We can all plan to do work, and then find our plans go wrong. There may be several reasons for this. How many of the following do *you* do?

Top time-wasting activities
1	Allowing (or encouraging) people to interrupt you.
2	Not having the information, handouts or textbook you need because you've lost them or lent them to someone else.
3	Chatting to people, making calls or sending texts when you should be working.
4	Getting distracted because you simply must keep checking out MySpace, Facebook or emails.
5	Putting off jobs until they are a total nightmare, then panicking.
6	Daydreaming.
7	Making a mess of something so you have to start all over again.

Planning and getting organised

The first step in managing your time is to plan ahead and be well organised. Some people are naturally good at this. They think ahead, write down their commitments in a diary or planner, and store their notes and handouts neatly and carefully so they can find them quickly.

How good are your working habits?

Talking to friends can take up a lot of time.

Improving your planning and organisational skills

1	Use a diary or planner to schedule working times into your weekdays and weekends.
2	Have a place for everything and everything in its place.
3	Be strict with yourself when you start work. If you aren't really in the mood, set a shorter time limit and give yourself a reward when the time is up.
4	Keep a diary in which you write down exactly what work you have to do.
5	Divide up long or complex tasks into manageable chunks and put each 'chunk' in your diary with a deadline of its own.
6	Write a 'to do' list if you have several different tasks. Tick them off as you go.
7	Always allow more time than you think you need for a task.

TRY THIS

Analyse your average day.

How many hours do you spend sleeping, eating, travelling, attending school or college, working and taking part in leisure activities?

How much time is left for homework and assignments?

Case study: Getting yourself organised

Lloyd and Rebecca are good friends. They sit next to each other in lessons and hang about together after college. Rebecca likes to chat a lot and constantly distracts Lloyd who likes the attention!

They are due to complete two assignments by the end of the week but neither of them has made much progress. One of the assignments involves researching and delivering a presentation, requiring a lot of planning and preparation.

They plan to work on the presentation together out of lesson time. However, when using the internet for research, Rebecca gets distracted by shopping sites and spends two hours looking for a new pair of shoes. Lloyd spends most of his time checking the football scores and listening to his favourite tunes.

By Wednesday, they are both feeling really stressed about the assignments, but have lessons all day. Lloyd needs to catch the bus to the library to get some books but sees his friends instead. He gets home quite late and is very tired.

On Thursday, they decide to skip lessons for a day and sneak round to Rebecca's house while her parents are at work. They manage to spend a few hours putting together the presentation.

The assignments are due in the following day, so they decide to stay up on Thursday night to complete them. However, Rebecca is unable to continue as she has a bad headache and Lloyd gets a phone call from a friend.

On Friday, when the assignments are due in, Rebecca forgets her USB stick. She has to miss the morning lesson to go home to fetch it and gets in trouble for being late. Lloyd is very nervous about his presentation because he hasn't practised it.

Because of factors like these, Lloyd and Rebecca often don't get their work in on time or complete it to the best of their capabilities. What time-wasters could Lloyd and Rebecca have avoided? You could make a list and write a note about how you would avoid each one.

TOP TIP

If you become distracted by social networking sites or email when you're working, set yourself a time limit of 10 minutes or so to indulge yourself.

BTEC FACT

If you have serious problems that are interfering with your ability to work or to concentrate, talk to your tutor. There are many ways in which BTEC learners who have personal difficulties can be supported to help them continue with their studies.

Activity: Managing time

1 The correct term for something you do in preference to starting a particular task is a 'displacement activity'. In the workplace this includes things like often going to the water cooler to get a drink, and constantly checking emails and so on online. People who work from home may tidy up, watch television or even cook a meal to put off starting a job.

Write down *your* top three displacement activities.

2 Today is Wednesday. Sajid has several jobs to do tonight and has started well by making a 'to do' list. He's worried that he won't get through all the things on his list and, because he works on Thursday and Friday evenings, that the rest will have to wait until Saturday.

a) Look through Sajid's list and decide which jobs are top priority and *must* be done tonight and which can be left until Saturday if he runs out of time.

b) Sajid is finding that his job is starting to interfere with his ability to do his assignments. What solutions can you suggest to help him?

> **Jobs to do**
>
> - File handouts from today's classes
>
> - Phone Tom (left early today) to tell him the time of our presentation tomorrow has been changed to 11 am
>
> - Research information online for next Tuesday's lesson
>
> - Complete table from rough notes in class today
>
> - Rewrite section of leaflet to talk about at tutorial tomorrow
>
> - Write out class's ideas for the charity of the year, ready for course representatives meeting tomorrow lunchtime
>
> - Redo handout Tom and I are giving out at presentation
>
> - Plan how best to schedule assignment received today – deadline 3 weeks
>
> - Download booklet from website ready for next Monday's class

Getting the most from work experience

On some BTEC First courses, all learners have to do a **work placement**. On others, they are recommended but not essential, or are required only for some optional units. If you are doing one, you need to prepare for it so that you get the most out of it. The checklists in this section will help.

Before you go checklist

1. Find out about the organisation by researching online.

2. Check that you have all the information you'll need about the placement.

3. Check the route you will need to take and how long it will take you. Always allow longer on the first day.

4. Check with your tutor what clothes are suitable and make sure you look the part.

5. Check that you know any rules or guidelines you must follow.

6. Check that you know what to do if you have a serious problem during the placement, such as being too ill to go to work.

7. Talk to your tutor if you have any special personal concerns.

8. Read the unit(s) that relate to your placement carefully. Highlight points you need to remember or refer to regularly.

9. Read the assessment criteria that relate to the unit(s) and use these to make a list of the information and evidence you'll need to obtain.

10. Your tutor will give you an official logbook or diary – or just use a notebook. Make notes each evening while things are fresh in your mind, and keep them safe.

While you're on work placement

Ideally, on your first day you'll be told about the organisation and what you'll be expected to do. You may even be allocated to one particular member of staff who will be your 'mentor'. However, not all workplaces operate like this and if everyone is very busy, your **induction** may be rushed. If so, stay positive and watch other people to see what they're doing. Then offer to help where you can.

BTEC FACT

If you need specific evidence from a work placement for a particular unit, your tutor may give you a logbook or work diary, and will tell you how you will be assessed in relation to the work you will do.

TRY THIS

You're on work experience. The placement is interesting and related to the job you want to do. However, you've been watching people most of the time and want to get more involved. Identify three jobs you think you could offer to do.

While you're there

1 Arrive with a positive attitude, knowing that you are going to do your best and get the most out of your time there.

2 Although you may be nervous at first, don't let that stop you from smiling at people, saying 'hello' and telling them your name.

3 Arrive punctually – or even early – every day. If you're delayed for any reason, phone and explain. Then get there as soon as you can.

4 If you take your mobile phone, switch it off when you arrive.

5 If you have nothing to do, offer to help someone who is busy or ask if you can watch someone who is doing a job that interests you.

6 Always remember to thank people who give you information, show you something or agree to you observing them.

7 If you're asked to do something and don't understand what to do, ask for it to be repeated. If it's complicated, write it down.

8 If a task is difficult, start it and then check back that you are doing it correctly before you go any further.

9 Obey all company rules, such as regulations and procedures relating to health and safety and using machinery, the use of IT equipment and access to confidential information.

10 Don't rush off as fast as you can at the end of the day. Check first with your mentor or supervisor whether you can leave.

TOP TIP

Observing people who are skilled at what they do helps you learn a lot, and may even be part of your **assignment brief.**

Coping with problems

Problems are rare but can happen. The most common ones are being bored because you're not given any work to do or upset because you feel someone is treating you unfairly. Normally, the best first step is to talk to your mentor at work or your supervisor. However, if you're very worried or upset, you may prefer to get in touch with your tutor instead – do it promptly.

Getting experience of work in applied science

Before starting your work experience, you should find out about your placement so that on your first day you:

- know what to expect
- are able to talk to people in a knowledgeable and interested way
- create a good impression with employees who are giving up their time to help you.

Your work experience

You will be going into a science-related workplace for your BTEC First placement. In preparation for your work experience, you will find it useful to make notes on the following things.

1 Find out about the place where you are going to do your work experience and make some notes.

2 How are you going to get there and how much will it cost?

3 What clothes will you wear?

4 What rules and regulations do you need to follow in your placement?

5 What is the contact telephone number if you are ill or late, and what reporting procedures do you need to follow?

_____

_____

_____

6 What should you do if you have any concerns before going on your placement?

_____

_____

_____

7 Which unit relates to the placement? Read it carefully. What important points do you need to remember?

_____

_____

_____

8 List the information and evidence you need to collect from your work experience placement. Read the grading criteria and make some notes.

_____

_____

_____

_____

9 What kinds of notes do you need to take each day, and how and where will you record these?

_____

_____

_____

Complete the following questionnaire to help you think about how you should conduct yourself when you are at your science-related work placement. Circle the correct answer.

While you are on your work experience placement what should you do if:

1 you have nothing to do?
   a) sit around and read a magazine
   b) offer to help someone who is busy
   c) go and get yourself a cup of coffee

2 you find a task difficult?
   a) carry on and don't ask anyone for any help
   b) check that you are doing it correctly and ask for help if you need to
   c) start worrying and burst into tears

3 you are late?
   a) just go in and hope nobody notices
   b) ring to tell your mentor you are on your way, then report in and apologise on your arrival
   c) don't bother going in at all

4 you get there and you don't like it?
   a) walk out
   b) think it may just be nerves – be positive as you know it will be worthwhile in the end
   c) be negative, sulk around and don't speak to anyone

5 you feel too ill to go into work?
   a) ring in as early as possible to say what is wrong and when you expect to be back at work
   b) don't do anything – they will know you are ill
   c) ring up at lunchtime and, if no one answers, don't bother ringing back

6 someone is really helpful and gives you some useful advice?
   a) avoid them because they are trying to tell you what to do again
   b) say thank you to them for their advice and ask more questions
   c) tell them to stop interfering because you know what you're doing

7 at the end of the day?
   a) sneak off 10 minutes early because you are going out that night
   b) just go anyway because someone else is leaving
   c) ask the supervisor or mentor if you are allowed to leave

Case study: Jack prepares for his placement

Jack will be starting his work experience in a week's time. He will be spending his placement in the Microbiology Laboratory at a hospital in Sheffield. His job description states that he will be shadowing the microbiologists.

He feels that he should prepare well so he knows what he is doing – he is a bit unsure about what is involved and, consequently, quite nervous. Jack speaks to his tutor about what the work placement entails. The tutor gives Jack a contact number for the workplace mentor who will be looking after him. Jack phones his mentor, Richard, and has this conversation:

Jack: 'Hello is that Richard? I'm Jack and I am coming to do some work experience with you. I would really like to know exactly what I will be doing so that I can prepare properly. I was also wondering what I should wear and if I need to bring anything with me?'

Richard: 'Hi, nice to speak to you Jack. I can certainly give you a little bit of an insight into what you will be doing. You will be shadowing the microbiologists to see how they perform microbiology techniques, including preparing plates and growing different samples from the hospital or from doctors' surgeries. Then you'll observe how these are analysed. We deal mainly with blood and urine samples from patients.

You will also see how the microbiologists identify different microorganisms using microscopes and other techniques. This allows them to pinpoint which microbes are making someone ill; knowledge that helps doctors to select the most appropriate treatment, for example a particular antibiotic.

Health and safety is really important when working in a microbiology laboratory, so you'll have to get to grips with a few different procedures.

You really need to wear some smart but practical clothes, for example black trousers and a shirt. We will provide you with a lab coat, gloves and face mask. You also need to bring something to take notes, a pen and maybe a calculator – you might be asked to carry out calculations when you're here. I hope this helps. If there's anything else you want to know just contact me.'

Jack: 'Thank you for your time. You've been really helpful. I will see you next Monday at 9 o'clock.'

In preparation for his work placement, Jack does some research on the internet. He finds the website for the NHS hospital where he will be working and also looks into what a microbiologist does. He checks his assignment brief for the unit and highlights anything he thinks is important. Jack also consults the bus and train timetables to find out the best way to get there, the times of the services and how much it will cost.

On Jack's first day, he sets off in good time. However, his bus is late so he rings Richard to warn him of the delay. Fortunately, Jack had made a note of the contact number. On his arrival Jack meets Richard in person and is introduced to the microbiology team. Jack is very polite, chats with staff, listens to what they have to say and asks lots of questions.

As Jack observes the microbiologists in their work, he takes notes in his diary and, from time to time, asks if he can do anything to help. At the end of the day, Jack asks if he can leave and thanks everyone for their time and help.

At home, Jack thinks back over his day and makes a few more notes in preparation for his assignment. He decides to have an early night so he can catch an earlier bus in the morning as he doesn't want to be late again.

Are there things that Jack did in preparation for his placement or during his work experience that you could do to help you to succeed in your placement and the assignment that follows?

Working with other people

Everyone finds it easy to work with people they like and far harder with those they don't. On your course you'll often be expected to work in a team to do a task. This gives you practice in working with different people.

You will be expected to:

- contribute to the task
- listen to other people's views
- adapt to other people's ways of working
- take responsibility for your own contribution
- agree the best way to resolve any problems.

These are quite complex skills. It helps if you understand the benefits to be gained by working cooperatively with other people and know the best way to achieve this.

BTEC FACT

An important part of your BTEC course is learning how to work positively and productively with other people.

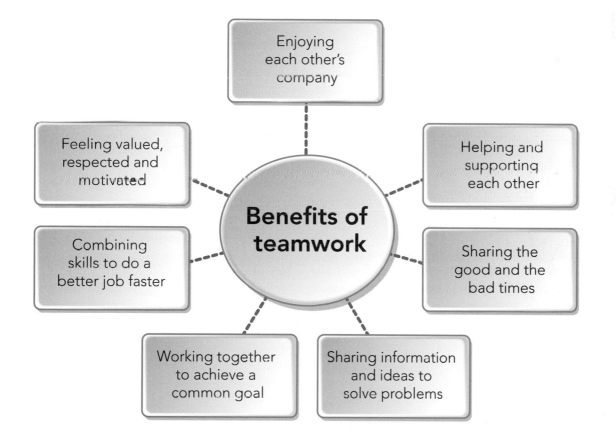

The benefits of good working relationships and teamwork

Golden rules for everyone (including the team leader!)

The secret of a successful team is that everyone works together. The role of the team leader is to make this as easy as possible by listening to people's views and coordinating everyone's efforts. A team leader is not there to give orders.

Positive teamwork checklist

- ✔ Be loyal to your team, including the team leader.
- ✔ Be reliable and dependable at all times.
- ✔ Be polite. Remember to say 'please' and 'thank you'.
- ✔ Think before you speak.
- ✔ Treat everyone the same.
- ✔ Make allowances for individual personalities. Give people 'space' if they need it, but be ready to offer support if they ask for it.
- ✔ Admit mistakes and apologise if you've done something wrong – learn from it but don't dwell on it.
- ✔ Give praise when it's due, give help when you can and thank people who help you.
- ✔ Keep confidences, and any promises that you make.

Do you:

a) shrug and say nothing in case he gets upset

b) ask why he didn't text you to give you warning

c) say that it's the last time you'll ever go anywhere with him and walk off?

Which do you think would be the most effective – and why?

Case study: Teamworking in Applied Science

As part of the BTEC First in Applied Science, a class of learners has been asked to work in teams of four for their next biology assignment. Working together as a 'genetic research team', each group has to prepare a poster on 'Variation' to present at a genetics and variation conference. Learners are expected to get together and complete this task for homework.

The tutor observes two of the groups as they work and makes notes on their performance to feed back on completion of the task.

Group 1

Straight away, Mohamed selects himself team leader and tells the other members of the group what they need to do. Sammy and Aisha don't mind this approach, but Tom doesn't like it as Mohamed hasn't let him make any decisions. Tom becomes fed up and won't do the job Mohamed has given him: to research information in the library. The other two girls in the group need this information in order to complete the poster for Mohamed who has

also elected himself to present the poster to the rest of the class. At the end of the lesson, this group hasn't got very far and has made no arrangements to meet up again to complete the poster.

Group 2

First, Aaron asks the team to vote for a team leader. They all agree it should be Aaron as he is a fair and good leader. Team members all set about their individual tasks, listening to each other's views on how the poster should look. They make a very good start on their planning and arrange to meet up in the library on Wednesday at 4pm. They swap email addresses and phone numbers in case they aren't able to make it. Aaron also asks his group to agree on an agenda for the next meeting, so they can get the work done quickly and have time to practise the presentation.

Which group do you think will get their poster completed in time to present at the next lesson? Why?

There are many benefits to be gained from working as a team.

Activity: Teamwork

1 Scientists are often required to work with other people in order to complete tasks. You may be asked to work in a team to make a group presentation, to plan and carry out an investigation or to prepare a questionnaire and collect data.

Look back at the tutor's comments about how well Groups 1 and 2 worked in teams (page 33). Now complete the following table. Put a tick if the team followed the rule for effective teamworking.

Teamworking rule Did the team …	Group 1	Group 2
… select a team leader?		
… share the work equally?		
… listen to the views of others?		
… take health and safety into account?		
… arrange meeting times?		
… agree on an agenda for next meeting?		
… collect contact details for team members?		

2 Now think about the teamworking skills that would be required when completing the following group task.

Imagine that, as part of a team of science writers working for BTEC, you have been asked to find out learners' views on this Study Skills Guide, which is provided as part of the BTEC First in Applied Science. You will need to consider how the team would create a questionnaire, distribute it, collect it back in, analyse the results and present a summary of the findings.

Use the table below to help you think about creating a questionnaire for the task. Some questions have already been inserted; complete the questionnaire using some of your own questions.

BTEC First in Applied Science Study Skills Guide Questionnaire		
Did you find the Study Skills Guide for Applied Science interesting?	Yes	No
Has the Study Skills Guide helped you develop skills that you need on this course?	Yes	No
Was the layout of the Study Skills Guide easy to follow?	Yes	No
	Yes	No
	Yes	No
	Yes	No
	Yes	No
How do you think the Study Skills Guide for Applied Science could be improved? For example, is there anything you would like to see in it that is not included at the moment?		

Think about how important it would be to use the rules for effective teamworking when completing this group task.

Teamworking rule The team should …	Very important	Not important
… select a team leader.		
… share the work equally.		
… listen to the views of others.		
… take health and safety into account.		
… arrange meeting times.		
… agree on an agenda for each meeting.		
… collect contact details for team members.		

In the space provided below, summarise what you feel are the most important aspects of teamworking for completing the questionnaire task.

How good are you at working with other people?

Did you manage to assess the importance of the rules for effective teamworking during this task? (Look at the table. Did you tick all the boxes?)

How could you use what you have learned about working effectively with others to help you to complete future team-based work or assessments?

Getting the most from special events

BTEC First courses usually include several practical activities and special events. These enable you to find out information, develop your skills and knowledge in new situations and enjoy new experiences. They may include visits to external venues, visits from specialist speakers, and team events.

This visit to a laboratory will allow the learner to see what kind of job he might be doing in the future.

Most learners enjoy the chance to do something different. You'll probably look forward to some events more than others. If you're ready to get actively involved, you'll usually gain the most benefit. It also helps to make a few preparations!

Case study: Visits and speakers

As part of his BTEC First in Applied Science, Scott is going on an excursion to the National Space Centre. He has always been interested in space travel and wants to study space science at university. Then, hopefully, he will get a job in this field.

Scott has an assignment to complete which requires information from the excursion. He is also hoping to write an article for a science magazine aimed at learners of his own age. For both projects, he will need to take lots of notes, collect leaflets and take photographs.

Think about what equipment he should take on the visit, the sort of information he might want to gather and how he should collect it.

Scott's tutor has also arranged for visiting speakers from three universities to talk to the learners about the variety of science-related degrees that they offer. Scott is really excited as two of the universities offer Space Science as a degree

course. He prepares some questions to ask the speakers so he can get all the information he needs. His questions are:

- How long is the course and what modules and topics are covered?

- What are the entry requirements of the course?

- Am I able to get onto the course with BTEC qualifications and, if so, what grades do I need?

- Would I have the opportunity to do any work experience as part of the course and, if so, with which companies?

- What are the possible career options for a graduate in this field?

Have you thought about what you want to do as a future career? What questions would you ask if a guest speaker came to your centre to talk about a degree course or career that interests you?

Special events checklist

✔ Check you understand how the event relates to your course.

✔ If a visit or trip is not something you would normally find very interesting, try to keep an open mind. You might get a surprise!

✔ Find out what you're expected to do, and any rules or guidelines you must follow, including about your clothes or appearance.

✔ Always allow enough time to arrive five minutes early, and make sure you're never late.

✔ On an external visit, make notes on what you see and hear. This is essential if you have to write about it afterwards, use your information to answer questions in an assignment or do something practical.

✔ If an external speaker is going to talk to your class, prepare a list of questions in advance. Nominate someone to thank the speaker afterwards. If you want to record the talk, it's polite to ask first.

✔ For a team event, you may be involved in planning and helping to allocate different team roles. You'll be expected to participate positively in any discussions, to talk for some (but not all) of the time, and perhaps to volunteer for some jobs yourself.

✔ Write up any notes you make as soon as you can – while you can still understand what you wrote!

TRY THIS

At the last minute, you're asked to propose a vote of thanks to a visiting speaker on behalf of your class. What would you say?

Activity: A visit from a guest speaker

A guest speaker from the Environment Agency is visiting your centre. The purpose of the visit is to help with the preparation for an assignment on global warming. How will you behave?

1. I will need to be equipped with:
   a) a pen and paper
   b) nothing; I will remember everything
   c) some work to be getting on with if I get bored.

2. I will:
   a) take as many relevant notes as possible while listening to the presentation
   b) just remember it all in my head; I don't need notes
   c) record the presentation using the video camera on my mobile. (What problems may this cause?)

3. If the guest speaker gives me leaflets I will:
   a) take them but throw them in the bin later
   b) take them and keep them safe so that I can use them for my assignment
   c) take them but not use them in my assignment.

4. During the presentation I will:
   a) speak to my friend about what we are doing at the weekend
   b) listen to the presentation, being quiet and respectful throughout
   c) try to complete one of my other assignments at the same time as listening.

5. At the end I will:
   a) not ask any questions as I feel stupid speaking out in front of everyone
   b) ask questions to clarify issues that I haven't fully understood, and ask pre-prepared questions on areas that interest me or are to do with my assignment
   c) ask totally irrelevant questions that are not related to the issues being discussed.

Resources and research

Understanding resources

Resources are items that help you do something. The most obvious one is money! To obtain your BTEC First award, however, your resources are rather different.

Different kinds of resources

Physical resources

Physical resources are things like textbooks, computers and any specialist equipment.

- Popular textbooks, laptops for home use and specialist equipment may need to be booked. Leaving it until the last minute is risky.
- You can ask for help if you don't know how to use resources properly.
- You should check what stationery and equipment you need at the start of your course and make sure you have it.
- You need to look after your resources carefully. This saves money and time spent replacing lost items.

People as resources

There are many people who can help you through your course:

- family members who help and support you
- your tutor
- friends in your group who collect handouts for you and phone you to keep you up-to-date when you're absent
- librarians and computer technicians, at your centre or your local library
- expert practitioners.

Expert practitioners

Expert practitioners have worked hard to be successful in their chosen area. They know the skills and knowledge needed to do the job properly. They can be invaluable when you're researching information. You can also learn a lot by watching them at work, especially if you can ask them questions about what they do, what they find hard and any difficulties they've had.

Observing expert practitioners allows you to see firsthand the kinds of skills you may want to develop.

Try to observe more than one expert practitioner:

- It gives you a better picture of what they do.
- No single job will cover all aspects of work that might apply to your studies.
- You may find some experts more approachable and easy to understand than others. For example, if someone is impatient because they're busy it may be difficult to ask them questions, or if someone works very quickly you may find it hard to follow what they're doing.

If you have problems, just note what you've learned and compare it with your other observations. And there's always the chance that you're observing someone who's not very good at their job! You'll only know this for certain if you've seen what people should be doing.

Activity: Creating your own resources lists

Creating resources lists encourages you to be organised, think ahead and make the most of opportunities.

1 What resources will you need to complete your assignments? Look through your assignment briefs and create a resource list for each one using the table below.

Assignment number	Resources required

2 Think about the people who might be useful to you when completing the BTEC First in Applied Science. How could they be helpful to you? Fill in the table.

Person	How could they be helpful?

3 Can you think of any expert practitioners working in science-related jobs who might be useful to you when completing your assignments? Fill in the table.

Unit/Assignment	Expert practitioner	How could they be useful?

Finding the information you need

The information explosion

There are lots of different ways to find out information – books, newspapers, magazines, TV, radio, CDs, DVDs, the internet. And you can exchange information with other people by texting, sending an email or phoning someone.

All this makes it much easier to obtain information. If you know what you're doing, you can probably find most of what you need sitting at a computer. But there are some dangers:

- Finding exactly what you want online takes skill. You need to know what you're doing.
- It's easy to get too much information and become overwhelmed.
- It's unlikely that everything you need will be available online.
- The information you read may be out of date.
- The information may be neither reliable nor true.

Define what you are trying to find. (The more precise you are, the more likely you are to find what you're looking for.)

Know where to look for it. (Remember: the internet is not the only source of information.)

Recognise when you have found appropriate information.

Know what to do with information once you've found it. (Make sure that you understand it, interpret it correctly and record the source where you found it.)

Know when to stop looking (especially if you have a deadline).

Finding and using information effectively

Before you start

There are four things that will help you look in the right place and target your search properly.

Ask yourself …	Because …	Example
Exactly what do I need to find out?	It will save you time and effort.	If you need information about accidents, you need to know what type of accident and over what time period.
Why do I need this information and who is going to read it?	This puts the task into context. You need to identify the best type of information to obtain and how to get it.	If you're making a poster or leaflet for children, you'll need simple information that can be presented in a graphical format. If, however, you're giving a workplace presentation on accidents, you'll need tables and graphs to illustrate your talk.
Where can I find it?	You need to consider whether your source is trustworthy and up to date. The internet is great, but you must check that the sites you use are reliable.	To find out about accidents in the workplace you could talk to the health and safety officer. To find examples of accidents in your local area you could look through back copies of your local newspaper in the library or newspaper offices.
What is my deadline?	You know how long you have to find the information and use it.	

TRY THIS

Schedule your research time by calculating backwards from the deadline date. Split the time you have 50/50 between searching for information and using it. This stops you searching for too long and getting lots of interesting material, but then not having the time to use it properly!

Your three main sources of information are:

- libraries or learning resource centres
- the internet
- asking other people, for example through interviews and questionnaires.

Researching in libraries

You can use the learning resource centre in your school or college, or a local public library. Public libraries usually have a large reference section with many resources available for loan, including CD-ROMs, encyclopaedias, government statistics, magazines, journals and newspapers, and databases such as Infotrac, which contains articles from newspapers and magazines over the last five years.

The librarian will show you how to find the resources you need and how to look up a specific book (or author) to check if it is available or is out on loan.

Some books and resources can only be used in the library itself; others can be taken out on short-term or long-term loan. You need to plan how to access and use the resources that are popular or restricted.

Using your library

✔ If your centre has an intranet you might be able to check which books and CD-ROMs are available without actually visiting the library.

✔ All libraries have photocopying facilities, so take enough change with you to copy articles that you can't remove. Write down the source of any article you photocopy, ie the name and the date of the publication.

✔ Learn how to keep a reference file (or bibliography) in which you store the details of all your sources and references. A bibliography must include CDs, DVDs and other information formats, not just books and magazines.

✔ If your search is complicated, go at a quiet time when the librarian can help you.

✔ Don't get carried away if you find several books that contain the information you need. Too many can be confusing.

✔ Use the index to find information quickly by searching for key words. Scan the index using several likely alternatives.

✔ Only use books that you find easy to understand. A book is only helpful if you can retell the information in your own words.

Researching online

A good search engine such as Google will help you find useful websites. They look for sites based on the information you enter in the search box. In some cases, such as Ask.co.uk, you may get the chance to refine your choice after entering your key words or question.

Finding information on a website

Wikipedia is a popular free online encyclopaedia. It has been criticised because entries may be inaccurate as members of the public can edit the site. However, Wikipedia is trying to prevent this by organising professional editing.

If you're not sure whether something you read is correct, or if there is anything strange about it, check it against information on another site. Make sure you ask your tutor's opinion, too.

With large websites, it can be difficult to find what you need. Always read the whole screen – there may be several menus in different parts of the screen.

To help you search, many large websites have:
- their own search facility or a site map that lists site content with links to the different pages
- links to similar sites where you might find more information. Clicking a link should open a new window, so you'll still be connected to the original site.

TRY THIS

Search engines don't just find websites. On Google, the options at the top of your screen include 'images', 'news' and 'maps'. If you click on 'more' and then 'even more', you'll find other options. You'll usually find the most relevant information if you use the UK version of a search engine. Only search the whole web if you deliberately want to include European and American information. To see this in action, go to www.pearsonhotlinks.co.uk, insert the express code 5797S and click on the link for this page.

There may be useful information and links at the top, foot or either side of a web page.

There are several other useful sites you could visit when researching online.

- **Directory sites** show websites in specific categories so you can focus your search at the start.
- **Forums** are sites, or areas of a website, where people post comments on an issue. They can be useful if you want to find out opinions on a topic. You can usually read them without registering.
- **News sites** include the BBC website as well as the sites for all the daily newspapers. Check the website of your local newspaper, too.

Printing information

- Only print information that you're sure will be useful. It's easy to print too much and find yourself drowning in paper.
- Make quick notes on your print-outs so that you remember why you wanted them. It will jog your memory when you're sorting through them later.
- If there's a printer-friendly option, use it. It will give you a print-out without unnecessary graphics or adverts.
- Check the bottom line of your print-outs. It should show the URL for that page of the website, and the date. You need those if you have to list your sources or if you want to quote from the page.

TRY THIS

To see how directory sites work go to www.pearsonhotlinks.co.uk, insert the express code 5797S and click on the link for this page.

TOP TIP

Bookmark any sites you use regularly by adding the URL to your browser. How to do this will depend on which browser you use, eg Internet Explorer, Firefox.

Researching by asking other people

You're likely to do this for two reasons:
- you need help from someone who knows a lot about a topic
- you need to find out several people's opinions on something.

Information from an expert

Explain politely why you are carrying out the investigation. Ask questions slowly and clearly about what they do and how they do it. If they don't mind, you could take written notes so you remember what they tell you. Put the name and title of the person, and the date, at the top. This is especially important if you might be seeing more than one person, to avoid getting your notes muddled up.

Ask if you may contact them again, in case there's anything you need to check. Write down their phone number or email address. Above all, remember to say 'thank you'!

Case study: Interviewing an expert

Ashley has been given an assignment on reproduction for one of the Biology units in the BTEC First in Applied Science. He plans to research the specific job roles of people who help childless couples have a baby. He telephones the local hospital to ask for some information. The receptionist puts Ashley through to one of the nurses working at the hospital. This is their conversation.

Ashley: 'Hello, my name is Ashley Hunt and I am doing an assignment as part of my BTEC First in Applied Science which involves finding out about people who work in jobs helping childless couples to have a baby. Please can you tell me if it would be possible to speak to some of the people involved in the process of in-vitro fertilisation or other assisted conception methods to find out what specific jobs they do?'

Nurse: 'Hello Ashley, the doctors are very busy at the moment, but I can give you a brief insight into the roles different people here have in helping childless couples to conceive.

The first person a childless couple will see is a doctor who will try to find out what the problem might be. Then, if the patients are referred for IVF or assisted conception,

specially trained nurses will deal with them. Nurses are involved in monitoring the couple on a regular basis, collecting sperm samples, taking blood samples, giving the woman drugs to help her to produce lots of eggs, carrying out scans and assisting doctors to carry out egg removal from the ovaries.

Once the eggs are removed, they go to the laboratory where reproductive scientists mix them with sperm, monitoring them carefully under a microscope.

Then doctors, with help from nurses, replace one or two healthy fertilised eggs back into the mother. Finally it is back to the nurses to take further scans and blood tests, all under the watchful eye of the professor in charge of the whole process. If you would like to come in, I may be able to arrange for you to look round at a later date.'

Ashley: 'That's really helpful, thank you. I would love to come in to do some further research. Can I ring you back to organise a visit? Bye.'

How can Ashley prepare for his visit to the hospital? What kinds of questions should he ask and what equipment will he need?

The opinions of several people

The easiest way to do this is with a questionnaire. You can either give people the questionnaire to complete themselves or interview them and complete it yourself. Professional interviewers often telephone people to ask questions, but at this stage it's not a good idea unless you know the people you're phoning and they're happy for you to do this.

Devising a questionnaire

1   Make sure it has a title and clear instructions.

2   Rather than ask for opinions, give people options, eg yes/no, maybe/always, never/sometimes. This will make it easier to analyse the results.

3   Or you can ask interviewees to give a score, say out of 5, making it clear what each number represents, eg 5 = excellent, 3 = very good.

4   Keep your questionnaire short so that your interviewees don't lose interest. Between 10 and 15 questions is probably about right, as long as that's enough to find out all you need.

5   Remember to add 'thank you' at the end.

6   Decide on the representative sample of people you will approach. These are the people whose views are the most relevant to the topic you're investigating.

7   Decide how many responses you need to get a valid answer. This means that the answer is representative of the wider population. For example, if you want views on food in your canteen, it's pointless only asking five people. You might pick the only five people who detest (or love) the food it serves.

Carrying out a questionnaire is an easy way of finding out what different people think about a certain issue or topic.

Activity: Research

Complete the following activities to help you get used to looking for information. Record all information sources you find.

1 Go to the library to find books and journals containing information on:
   - cells and cell functions
   - the Solar System
   - the Periodic Table.

2 Use the internet to search for information about different careers in science.

3 Contact your local NHS hospital to find out what kind of work experience placements are on offer.

4 Over lunch, ask other people on your course about the science-related careers or further studies they want to do in the future.

Keeping a logbook

Using your logbook to record important information

You will benefit greatly from keeping a diary or logbook to record all submission and resubmission dates for each assignment and to note whether you have gained a pass, merit or distinction at each submission.

You could create your own logbook using Template A on page 50. Use a chart like this to log all the details concerning your assignments.

Put this document into a special section of your working file, perhaps at the front, so that you can easily find out information about forthcoming submission dates. You will also be able to see at a glance which assignments you have passed (at pass, merit or distinction) and which ones need further work.

Some assignments may be more challenging than others, so you may find that you need extra help. Find out if there are any workshops or support sessions running on your course where you can go for help. Make a note of these sessions in Template B (page 50), recording the relevant details so that you do not forget to attend.

Template A

Unit number	Assignment number and title/ initials of tutor	Hand out date	First submission date	Second submission date	Pass/fail (state grade for each criterion)

Template B

Workshop/support session	Time	Date	Tutor	Room

Managing your information

Whether you've found lots of information or only a little, assessing what you have and using it wisely is very important. This section will help you avoid the main pitfalls.

Organising and selecting your information

Organising your information

The first step is to organise your information so that it's easy to use.
- Make sure your written notes are neat and have a clear heading – it's often useful to date them too.
- Note useful pages in any books or magazines you have borrowed.
- Highlight relevant parts of any handouts or leaflets.
- Work out the results of any questionnaires you've used.

Selecting your information

Re-read the **assignment brief** or instructions you were given to remind yourself of the exact wording of the question(s) and divide your information into three groups:
1 Information that is totally relevant.
2 Information that is not as good, but could come in useful.
3 Information that doesn't match the questions or assignment brief very well but that you kept because you couldn't find anything better!

Check there are no obvious gaps in your information against the questions or assignment brief. If there are, make a note of them so that you know exactly what you still have to find. Although it's ideal to have everything you need before you start work, don't delay if you're short of time.

Putting your information in order

Putting your information in a logical order means you can find what you want easily. It will save you time in the long run. This is doubly important if you have lots of information and will be doing the work over several sessions.

You should keep your folders well organised, with important information regarding your course filed in a special section for future reference.

Case study: Getting organised

Walik is very competitive and quite able, but not very good at organising himself or his work. He is eager to get going and complete his first assignment to distinction criteria – he wants to be the best in the class. When he is given the first assignment, he decides to make a start on the distinction criteria straight away.

'I'm doing the distinction criteria first; that will get me a distinction at the end of the year,' he says to his tutor, even though she has advised the class to start with the pass criteria.

When Walik submits the assignment, the tutor finds that he has completed all of the distinction criteria, but not to a very good standard. In addition to this, he has not completed any of the merit criteria and only half of the pass criteria, meaning that he has failed overall.

On marking Walik's work, the tutor also finds that he has not referenced any of his written work, diagrams or photographs. Walik is given written feedback to help him improve this and future assignments.

When Walik reads the feedback, he decides to try the assignment again by starting with the pass criteria and then progressing through the merit and distinction criteria. This time, he needs to reference all of his work but, due to his disorganised nature, he has not kept notes of the website addresses or titles of the books and newspapers he used. In addition, he did not file any of the handouts given out in class and has left his folder in a cupboard at home untouched.

It took Walik hours to find all the information in the first place, and now he has to hunt round again for the references.

What tips would you give Walik on how to organise his information to save time and to ensure he passes assignments?

TOP TIP

Add a separate section to your ring binder for any important information regarding your Applied Science assignments, including the hand-in dates and useful websites.

Activity: Organising your files

You will need to put your information in order and keep it safe so that you can find it easily when you need it for assignments, other homework or for lessons later in the course.

Choose one of your assignments, start looking for relevant information and sort it into piles. Then start to organise the information further by doing the following tasks. Make notes as you go, and sign and date each task as you complete it.

1 Create a folder in 'favourites' on the tool bar and give it an appropriate name: for example 'Assignment 1 Unit 3 websites'. Save any relevant websites in this folder for future reference.

2 As you collect useful books, make a note of the references including page numbers where you have found valuable information. Do this on a separate sheet of paper at the front of the section for this unit in your file.

3 When you finish with a book, journal or website, keep it separate from the resources you still need to look through.

4 Re-read the information you have collected, thinking about how it fits into the assignment. Make a note of this in the front of the unit section of your folder.

5 Always keep an assignment in the relevant section of your folder between work sessions to ensure you don't lose or damage it.

Interpreting and presenting your information

The next stage is to use your information to prepare the document and/or oral presentation you have to give. There are four steps:

1 Understand what you're reading.

2 Interpret what you're reading.

3 Know the best form in which to produce the information, bearing in mind the purpose for which it is required.

4 Create the required document so that it's in a suitable layout with correct spelling and punctuation.

Understanding what you read

As a general rule, never use information you don't understand. However, nobody understands complex or unfamiliar material the first time they read it, especially if they just scan through it quickly. Before you reject it, try this:

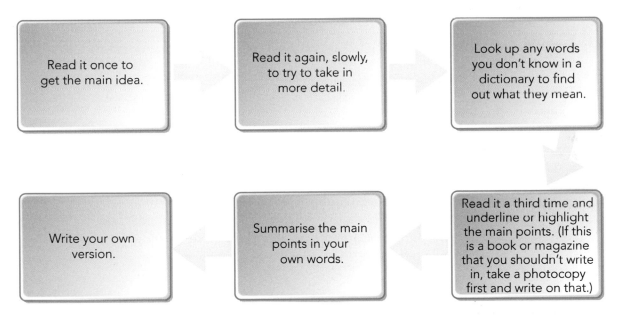

Read it once to get the main idea. → Read it again, slowly, to try to take in more detail. → Look up any words you don't know in a dictionary to find out what they mean. ↓

Write your own version. ← Summarise the main points in your own words. ← Read it a third time and underline or highlight the main points. (If this is a book or magazine that you shouldn't write in, take a photocopy first and write on that.)

Special note: Show both the article and your own version to your tutor to check your understanding. This will help you identify any points you missed out and help you improve your skills of interpreting and summarising.

Understanding unfamiliar information

Interpreting what you read

Interpreting what you read is different from understanding it. This is because you can't always take it for granted that something you read means what it says. The writer may have had a very strong or biased opinion, or may have exaggerated for effect. This doesn't mean that you can't use the information.

BTEC FACT

In your assignments, it's better to separate opinions from facts. If you're quoting someone's views, make this clear. (See also page 55.)

Strong opinions and bias

People often have strong points of view about certain topics. This may be based on reliable facts, but not always! We can all jump to conclusions that may not be very logical, especially if we feel strongly about something.

Things aren't always what they seem to be. Are these boys fighting or are they having a good time?

TRY THIS

There are many scare stories in the media about issues such as immigration, children's reading ability or obesity. Next time you're watching television and these are discussed, see if you can spot biased views, exaggeration and claims without any supporting evidence.

Exaggeration

Many newspapers exaggerate facts to startle and attract their readers.

LOCAL FIRM DOUBLES STAFF IN TWO WEEKS!

This newspaper headline sounds very positive. You could easily think it means that employment is growing and there are more jobs in your area. Then you read on, and find the firm had only four staff and now has eight!

Tables and graphs

You need to be able to interpret what the figures mean, especially when you look at differences between columns or rows. For example, your friend might have an impressive spreadsheet that lists his income and expenditure. In reality, it doesn't tell you much until you add the figures up and subtract one from the other. Only then can you say whether he is getting into debt. And even if he is, you need to see his budget over a few months, rather than just one which may be exceptional.

Choosing a format

You may have been given specific instructions about the format and layout of a document you have to produce, in which case life is easy as long as you follow them! If not, think carefully about the best way to set out your information so that it is clear.

TOP TIP

Never make assumptions or jump to conclusions. Make sure you have all the evidence to support your views.

Different formats	Example
text	when you write in paragraphs or prepare a report or summary
graphical	a diagram, graph or chart
pictorial	a drawing, photograph, cartoon or pictogram
tabular	numerical information in a table

The best method(s) will depend on the information you have, the source(s) of your material and the purpose of the document – a leaflet for schoolchildren needs graphics and pictures to make it lively, whereas a report to company shareholders would be mainly in text form with just one or two graphs.

Stating your sources

Whatever format you use, if you are including other people's views, comments or opinions, or copying a table or diagram from another publication, you must state the source by including the name of the author, publication or the web address. This can be in the text or as part of a list at the end. Failure to do this (so you are really pretending that other people's work is your own) is known as **plagiarism**. It is a serious offence with penalties to match.

Text format

Creating written documents gets easier with practice. These points should help.

TOP TIP

Don't just rely on your spellchecker. It won't find a word spelled wrongly that makes another valid word (eg from/form), so you must proofread everything. And remember to check whether it is set to check American English or British English. There are some spelling differences.

Golden rules for written documents

1. Think about who will be reading it, then write in an appropriate language and style.

2. Ensure it is technically correct, ie no wrong spellings or bad punctuation.

3. Take time to make it look good, with clear headings, consistent spacing and plenty of white space.

4. Write paragraphs, each with a different theme. Leave a line space between each one.

5. If you have a lot of separate points to mention, use bullets or numbered points. Numbered points show a certain order or quantity (step 1, step 2, etc). Use bullet points when there is no suggested order.

6. Only use words that you understand the meaning of, or it might look as if you don't know what you mean.

7. Structure your document so that it has a beginning, middle and end.

8. Prepare a draft and ask your tutor to confirm you are on the right track and are using your information in the best way.

Graphical format

Most people find graphics better than a long description for creating a quick picture in the viewer's mind. There are several types of graphical format, and you can easily produce any of these if you have good ICT skills.

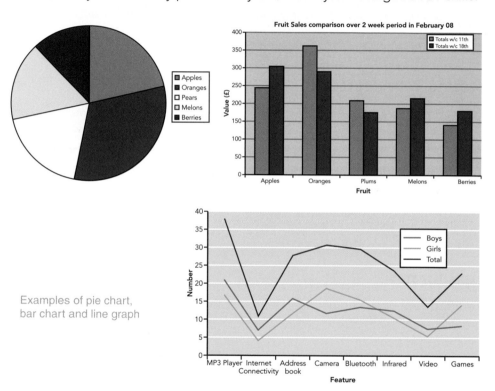

Examples of pie chart, bar chart and line graph

Pictorial format

Newspapers and magazines use pictures to illustrate situations and reduce the amount of words needed. It doesn't always have to be photographs though. For example, a new building may be sketched to show what it will look like.

A pictogram or pictograph is another type of pictorial format, such as charts which use the image of an object (fruit, coins, even pizzas) to represent data, such as the number eaten or amount spent.

Tabular format

A table can be an easy way to communicate information. Imagine a retailer preparing information about the items in stock. Text would be difficult to understand and comparisons between stock levels and sales would be almost impossible to make. A table, however, would easily show the fastest-selling items.

Tables are also ideal if you are showing rankings – such as best-selling music or books.

Bestsellers list – September 2009

Position	Title	Author	Imprint	Publication
1 (New)	Lost Symbol,The	Brown, Dan	Bantam Press	15-Sep-2009
2 (1)	Complaints, The	Rankin, Ian	Orion	03-Sep-2009
3 (New)	Return Journey, The	Binchy, Maeve	Orion	17-Sep-2009
4 (7)	Sapphire	Price, Katie	Century	30-Jul-2009
5 (9)	Wolf Hall	Mantel, Hilary	Fourth Estate	30-Apr-2009
6 (3)	Week in December, A	Faulks, Sebastian	Hutchinson	03-Sep-2009
7 (2)	Alex Cross's Trial	Patterson, James	Century	10-Sep-2009
8 (4)	White Queen, The	Gregory, Philippa	Simon & Schuster Ltd	18-Aug-2009
9 (5)	Even Money	Francis, Dick & Francis, Felix	Michael Joseph	03-Sep-2009
10 (8)	206 Bones	Reichs, Kathy	William Heinemann	27-Aug-2009

National newspaper circulation – September 2009

	August 2009	August 2008	% change on last year	August 09 (without bulks)	March 2009 – August 2009	% change on last year
Sun	3,128,501	3,148,792	-0.64	3,128,501	3,052,480	-2.25
Daily Mail	2,171,686	2,258,843	-3.86	2,044,079	2,178,462	-4.45
Daily Mirror	1,324,883	1,455,270	-8.96	1,324,883	1,331,108	9.44
Daily Star	886,814	751,494	18.01	886,814	855,511	16.65
The Daily Telegraph	814,087	860,298	-5.37	722,644	807,328	-6.73
Daily Express	730,234	748,664	-2.46	730,234	727,824	-1.32
Times	576,185	612,779	-5.97	529,746	588,471	-4.63
Financial Times	395,845	417,570	-5.2	365,269	411,098	-6.7
Daily Record	347,302	390,197	-10.99	345,277	350,306	-10.59
Guardian	311,387	332,587	-6.37	311,387	332,790	-4.11
Independent	187,837	230,033	-18.34	148,551	198,445	-16.76

Activity: Presenting data

Scientists have to produce reports on their scientific investigations, including a brief introduction and aim, description or diagram of the equipment, outline of the method, health and safety measures taken, a table of data, perhaps a graph, and then a conclusion to interpret the results. Finally, a report would contain an evaluation to assess the success of the investigation in addressing the aims, with recommendations for improvements in the method or further investigations.

Try the following activities to help you to practise some aspects of writing up a scientific investigation.

Using a table to present data

Sarah carried out an experiment to investigate the effect of temperature on the action of amylase (an enzyme which breaks down starch to produce glucose). Iodine solution turns blue/black if starch is present.

In this experiment, a mixture of starch and iodine starts off blue/black in colour. Amylase is added. Once all the starch has been broken down by the amylase, the blue/black colour of the iodine disappears.

Sarah timed the disappearance of the blue/black colour at different temperatures. She repeated the experiment twice at each temperature, making notes of her results.

Time taken for blue/black colour to disappear at different temperatures

Experiment 1	Experiment 2
4° took 7.5 mins	4° took 7 mins
22° took 3.5 mins	22° took 4 mins
37° took 3 mins	37° took 2.4 mins
80° didn't work	80° didn't work
90° didn't work	90° didn't work

Using a pencil and ruler, create a table to display this data. Make sure you include the following:

- a title
- all the data
- an average column
- clear headers in each column
- units in each column.

Producing a graph to present your information

When writing a report of a scientific investigation, scientists have to decide which type of graph is most appropriate for each set of data.

In the BTEC First in Applied Science you will probably come across these graphs:

- Line graphs – use a line graph when you have a set of data that is continuous, for example the effect of temperature or pH on enzyme activity. Line graphs should include each data point plotted clearly and accurately with an 'X'. If the points form a curve, then draw a smooth freehand curve of best fit. Make sure your curve includes as many points as possible, with an equal number of points on either side of the curve. If the points form a straight line, use a ruler to connect them.

- Bar charts – use a bar chart when you have data with a fixed value, for example UK annual birth rate or the electrical conductivity of different metals.

Using Sarah's data, draw a labelled graph in the space provided on the next page. Make sure you:
- choose the appropriate type of graph
- choose simple scales to help you plot the data
- give the graph a title
- label both the x- and y-axes
- put units on both axes
- plot your data carefully and accurately.

TOP TIP

Remember, the variable you change always goes along the bottom of the graph on the x-axis and the results you collect go on the y axis.

Interpreting your data and forming a conclusion

Making a conclusion involves producing a summary of what you have found out in the table of results and by plotting a graph. You have to look for patterns in the data and describe these in words.

Here is an example of a conclusion that was written using data from another experiment:

The table shows that the heart rate before exercise is lower than during exercise. The heart rate rises to 140 beats per minute during exercise, as opposed to 76 beats per minute at rest.

When a man walks uphill on a treadmill at the same speed and incline for 20 minutes, the graph shows a sharp increase at the start of the exercise, up to 140 beats per minute. Heart rate then levels off and stays at around that rate for the duration of the exercise

Now use the table and graph you produced from Sarah's data to write a conclusion in the space provided at the top of the next page.

Evaluating your results

In a scientific report, 'to evaluate' means to interpret the quality of the results using all the information collected and any previously documented scientific evidence that backs up the claims you are making. Usually, an evaluation also includes suggested improvements to the method, a discussion of any strange or anomalous results, and a judgement on how well your investigation went.

You may need to read up on enzyme activity to help you complete this part of the activity. Produce a brief evaluation for Sarah's results using the information she collected, and the table and graph you produced. There is no need to include a judgement on the success of the experiment in this case.

Making presentations

Presentations help you to learn communication skills.

Some people hate the idea of standing up to speak in front of an audience. This is quite normal, and you can use the extra energy from nerves to improve your performance.

Presentations aren't some form of torture devised by your tutor! They are included in your course because they help you learn many skills, such as speaking in public and preparing visual aids. They also help you practise working as a team member and give you a practical reason for researching information. And it can be far more enjoyable to talk about what you've found out rather than write about it!

There's a knack to preparing and giving a presentation so that you use your energies well, don't waste time, don't fall out with everyone around you and keep your stress levels as low as possible. Think about the task in three stages: preparation, organisation and delivery.

Preparation

Start your initial preparations as soon as you can. Putting them off will only cause problems later. Discuss the task in your team so that everyone is clear about what has to be done and how long they have to do it in.

Divide any research fairly among the team, allowing for people's strengths and weaknesses. You'll also need to agree:

- which visual aids would be best
- which handouts you need and who should prepare them
- where and when the presentation will be held, and what you should wear
- what questions you might be asked, both individually and as a team, and how you should prepare for them.

Once you've decided all this, carry out the tasks you've been allocated to the best of your ability and by the deadline agreed.

TOP TIP

Keep visual aids simple but effective and check any handouts carefully before you make lots of copies.

Organisation

This is about the planning you need to do as a team so that everything will run smoothly on the day.

Delivery

This refers to your performance during the presentation. Being well prepared and well organised helps to stop you panicking. If you're very nervous at the start, take a few deep breaths and concentrate on the task, not yourself. It's quite normal to be nervous at the start but this usually fades once you get under way. You might even enjoy it …

TOP TIP

Never read from prepared prompt cards! Look at the audience when you're talking and smile occasionally. If you need to use prompt cards as a reminder, write clearly so that you need only glance at them.

TOP TIP

Remember, the audience always makes allowances for some nerves!

Case study: Producing a presentation

Danielle and Stephanie have each been asked to produce a presentation entitled 'Interdependence and the environment' for an assignment.

Stephanie thinks the easiest way is to get some A3 paper and a couple of coloured pens to create a quick presentation.

Stephanie's plan is as follows:

- use one piece of A3 paper and two coloured pens (yellow and green)
- write as much as I can get onto the paper – writing may need to be quite small
- use a couple of books
- include one picture if there is space – no need to label it
- stick the page on the board during the presentation.

Danielle decides she would like to do really well in this assignment, aiming for a distinction grade. She knows she will have to plan well, thinking carefully about how she will present her information to make sure the other learners find it easy to read and interesting to listen to.

Danielle creates the following plan:

- use PowerPoint to create the presentation – make sure a computer and whiteboard are available

- use a font size of 24 or greater, so people can see clearly
- use black or dark-coloured writing
- choose an interesting background
- have a clear title
- keep the writing to a minimum – use bullet points
- include referenced diagrams and photographs from books, internet and journals
- include all the information required to complete the pass, merit and distinction criteria
- make additional notes for each slide and learn them, so that I can expand on the information on the slides and answer any questions at the end.

Think about whose plan was better and say why.

What are the benefits of using PowerPoint to create a presentation rather than pens and paper?

Activity: Organising your presentation

1 Your task is to prepare, organise and deliver a presentation on 'Famous scientists and their discoveries'.

Prepare for the presentation by making a plan. Use bullet points to note what equipment you will need.

2 Think about and make notes on how you will organise:

○ yourself

○ your equipment and resources

○ the delivery of the presentation itself.

3 Put ticks in the appropriate boxes to show whether you agree or disagree with the following tips for delivering a presentation.

Tip	Agree	Disagree
face the audience		
speak clearly and loudly		
read off the board, speaking quietly		
do not look at the audience		
be prepared to answer questions at the end		
practise the presentation		
stand in front of the presentation		

4 Bearing in mind those tips you disagree with, discuss how you could improve your technique to make your presentation better.

Your assessments
The importance of assignments

All learners on BTEC First courses are assessed by means of **assignments**. Each one is designed to link to specific **learning outcomes** and **grading criteria**. At the end of the course, your assignment grades put together determine your overall grade.

To get the best grade you can, you need to know the golden rules that apply to all assignments, then how to interpret the specific instructions.

10 golden rules for assignments

1. Check that you understand the instructions.

2. Check whether you have to do all the work on your own, or if you will do some as a member of a group. If you work as a team, you need to identify which parts are your own contributions.

3. Always write down any verbal instructions you are given.

4. Check the final deadline and any penalties for not meeting it.

5. Make sure you know what to do if you have a serious personal problem, eg illness, and need an official extension.

6. Copying someone else's work (**plagiarism**) is a serious offence and is easy for experienced tutors to spot. It's never worth the risk.

7. Schedule enough time for finding out the information and doing initial planning.

8. Allow plenty of time between talking to your tutor about your plans, preparations and drafts, and the final deadline.

9. Don't panic if the assignment seems long or complicated. Break it down into small, manageable chunks.

10. If you suddenly get stuck, ask your tutor to talk things through with you.

Case study: Understanding assessment

When Sasha started the BTEC First she was not sure about how her work would be assessed. At the first tutorial session the programme manager talked about portfolios, learning outcomes, specifications, grading criteria, key words and evidence.

It all seemed very confusing and Sasha doubted whether she would be able to cope with it all. There seemed to be no examinations and success was all down to presenting the correct coursework in order to pass the course.

'I was really confused when I started the course and mentioned this to my tutor at the end of the first week. He was very sympathetic and said that I would get lots of help putting together my unit portfolios and tracking my grades. He showed me the work of a learner who had completed the course last year and explained how their evidence was tracked against the grading criteria.

I then realised that the term "grading criteria" is just a technical way of telling you what you need to do – a bit like when I play snooker and have to take the colours in a particular order. You can't pot the black before taking the pink – you can't get a merit for a grading criterion before you have achieved a pass.

My tutor told me just to concentrate on learning about the technical stuff being taught – my portfolio-building skills would improve over a period of time. I felt much happier and took up his suggestion of reviewing my progress at the end of each month or when I hit a problem.'

Interpreting the instructions

Most assignments start with a **command word** – describe, explain, evaluate, etc. These words relate to how complex the answer should be.

Command words

Learners often don't do their best because they read the command words but don't understand exactly what they have to do. The tables on this page and the next show you what is required for each grade when you see a particular command word.

Command words and obtaining a pass

Complete …	Complete a form, diagram or drawing.
Demonstrate …	Show that you can do a particular activity.
Describe …	Give a clear, straightforward description that includes all the main points.
Identify …	Give all the basic facts relating to a certain topic.
List …	Write a list of the main items (not sentences).
Name …	State the proper terms related to a drawing or diagram.
Outline …	Give all the main points, but without going into too much detail.
State …	Point out or list the main features.

Examples:
- **List** the main features on your mobile phone.
- **Describe** the best way to introduce a visiting researcher.
- **Outline** the procedures you follow to keep your computer system secure.

Command words and obtaining a merit

Analyse …	Identify the factors that apply, and state how these are linked and how each of them relates to the topic.
Comment on …	Give your own opinions or views.
Compare … **Contrast …**	Identify the main factors relating to two or more items and point out the similarities and differences.
Competently use …	Take full account of information and feedback you have obtained to review or improve an activity.
Demonstrate …	Prove you can carry out a more complex activity.
Describe …	Give a full description including details of all the relevant features.
Explain …	Give logical reasons to support your views.
Justify …	Give reasons for the points you are making so that the reader knows what you're thinking.
Suggest …	Give your own ideas or thoughts.

Examples:
- **Explain** why mobile phones are so popular.
- **Describe** the different information needs of a member of the public and a scientific researcher.

TRY THIS

Check the command word you are likely to see for each of your units in the **grading grid** in advance. This tells you the **grading criteria** for the unit so that you know the evidence you will have to present.

- **Suggest** the type of procedures your employer would need to introduce to keep the IT system secure.

Command words and obtaining a distinction

Analyse ...	Identify several relevant factors, show how they are linked, and explain the importance of each.
Compare ... **Contrast ...**	Identify the main factors in two or more situations, then explain the similarities and differences, and in some cases say which is best and why.
Demonstrate ...	Prove that you can carry out a complex activity taking into account information you have obtained or received to adapt your original idea.
Describe ...	Give a comprehensive description which tells a story to the reader and shows that you can apply your knowledge and information correctly.
Evaluate ...	Bring together all your information and make a judgement on the importance or success of something.
Explain ...	Provide full details and reasons to support the arguments you are making.
Justify ...	Give full reasons or evidence to support your opinion.
Recommend ...	Weigh up all the evidence to come to a conclusion, with reasons, about what would be best.

Examples:

- **Evaluate** the features and performance of your mobile phone.
- **Analyse** the role of careful planning in contributing to an organisation's success.
- **Justify** the main features on the website of a research agency of your choice.

TOP TIP

Think of assignments as an opportunity to demonstrate what you've learned and to get useful feedback on your work.

Case study: Understanding command words

Paul collects an assignment on 'Energy' for his BTEC First in Applied Science. He sees that he hasn't passed but has received detailed feedback from his tutor. The comments read:

'Paul, you have not passed the assignment this time because you do not understand what the different command words mean.

For a pass, you should have described the different types of radiation, including non-ionising and ionising radiation, but you just made a list instead.

For a merit, you should have compared the efficiency of energy generated from different sources, but unfortunately you just gave a simple description of one source.

For a distinction, you should have assessed how to minimise energy losses when transmitting electricity and when converting it into other forms for consumer applications, but you have discussed this instead.

Please re-do the assignment for all the criteria and resubmit for the next deadline date.'

Paul is very confused so goes to see the tutor to ask where he went wrong and what the different command words mean. She tells him to look up the meanings of these command words in his Study Skills Guide, to help him re-do the assignment for the pass, merit and distinction criteria.

Paul completes his resubmission and is delighted to get a distinction on the second attempt.

Activity: Definitions

1. Look at pages 66 and 67 of this Study Skills Guide and, using your own words, write down what the following command words mean.

   ○ analyse

   ○ analyse

   ○ suggest

   ○ compare and contrast

   ○ justify

   ○ outline

   ○ demonstrate

   ○ describe

   ○ evaluate

   ○ list.

2. Using pages 66 and 67 give the correct command word for each of the following definitions:

   ○ Give all the main points but without going into too much detail.

   ○ Point out or list the main features.

   ○ Give your own opinions or views.

   ○ Take full account of information and feedback you have obtained to review or improve an activity.

- Give logical reasons to support your views.

- Weigh up all the evidence to come to a conclusion, with reasons, about what would be best.

- Identify several relevant factors, show how they are linked and explain the importance of each.

- Prove that you can carry out a complex activity, taking into account information you have obtained or received to adapt your original idea.

3. Complete the following checklist which is based on the 10 golden rules for assignments. Following these rules will ensure that you get the best possible grade on your assignments. Make several copies of the blank table and complete it every time you have to do an assignment.

	Assignment no.
I understand the instructions.	
I know if I am working on my own or in a group.	
I have written down any verbal instructions given to me by my tutor.	
I know the final deadline date and the penalty for not meeting it.	
I have made an agreement for an extension (If required).	
I have done adequate preparation for my assignment.	
I have broken this assignment into smaller, manageable chunks.	
I have spoken to my tutor early about plans, preparation and deadlines for this assignment.	
I have asked the tutor to clarify any problems or misunderstandings.	
It is all my own work and nothing is copied.	
I have referenced all my work.	

After each assignment, you should complete your own BTEC First **Recording your Achievement** form. This allows you to see your predicted overall grade. The form will be given to you by your tutor and can also be downloaded from the Edexcel website. Go to www.pearsonhotlinks.co.uk, insert the express code 5797S and click on the link for this activity.

TOP TIP

Read through all the command words to make sure you understand what you are expected to do to get the best possible grades in future assignments.

Sample assignment

Sample assignment front sheet

Complete the front sheet before submitting work by adding your name, signature and the date.

Ensure you hand work in on time. Your centre will have rules for you to follow on how to do this.

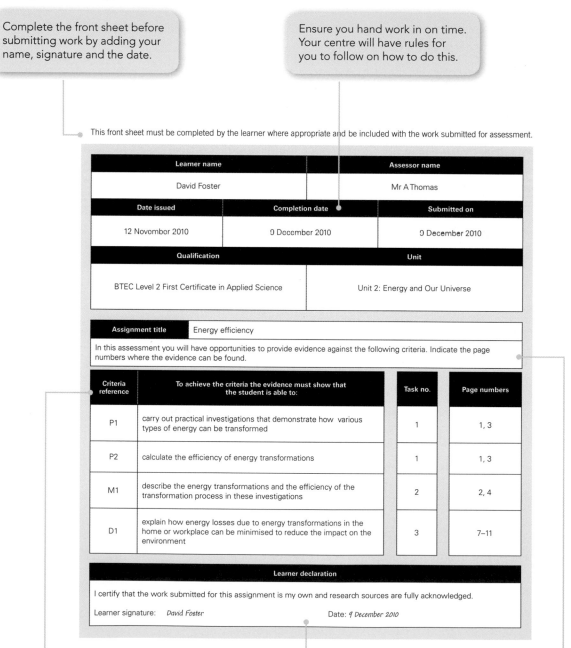

This front sheet must be completed by the learner where appropriate and be included with the work submitted for assessment.

Learner name		Assessor name	
David Foster		Mr A Thomas	

Date issued	Completion date	Submitted on
12 November 2010	9 December 2010	9 December 2010

Qualification	Unit
BTEC Level 2 First Certificate in Applied Science	Unit 2: Energy and Our Universe

Assignment title	Energy efficiency

In this assessment you will have opportunities to provide evidence against the following criteria. Indicate the page numbers where the evidence can be found.

Criteria reference	To achieve the criteria the evidence must show that the student is able to:	Task no.	Page numbers
P1	carry out practical investigations that demonstrate how various types of energy can be transformed	1	1, 3
P2	calculate the efficiency of energy transformations	1	1, 3
M1	describe the energy transformations and the efficiency of the transformation process in these investigations	2	2, 4
D1	explain how energy losses due to energy transformations in the home or workplace can be minimised to reduce the impact on the environment	3	7–11

Learner declaration

I certify that the work submitted for this assignment is my own and research sources are fully acknowledged.

Learner signature: *David Foster*   Date: *9 December 2010*

In order to satisfy the assessment process, it is extremely important that criteria in this table are met in a way that provides specific evidence relating to each task.

Remember that plagiarism is not permitted and you should not copy other people's work. Make sure you reference all phrases, illustrations and text taken from other works using your centre's chosen method of referencing.

You must provide specific evidence, based on the given criteria for this particular assignment. You will be given guidance on the different ways that you can provide this evidence in the brief itself.

Sample assignment brief

The scenario allows you to role-play the part of someone who works in a science-based job. It states why you are completing the assignment and what is expected of you.

Keep referring back to the assignment tasks and grading criteria to ensure you are on the right track when tackling the assignment.

Unit title	Unit 2: Energy and Our Universe
Qualification	BTEC Level 2 First Certificate in Applied Science
Start date	12 November 2010
Deadline date	9 December 2010
Assessor	Mr A Thomas

Assignment title	Energy efficiency

The purpose of this assignment is to:
enable you to appreciate forms of energy and energy transformations that occur in the home or workplace, using practical investigation and calculation methods.

Scenario
As a technician working for Energy Plus, a leading supplier of energy in the UK, you have been given the task of investigating energy transformations and calculating the efficiency of typical household and workplace devices. Your findings will be used by the company to deliver consumer advice.

Task 1
Carry out practical investigations that demonstrate how various types of energy can be transformed, and calculate the efficiency of the energy transformations.

To do this, set up practical equipment to safely investigate the following energy transformation devices:
• an electrical motor
• a filament lamp.

Produce a risk assessment for each activity using the forms provided.

Then carry out your practical investigations. Your assessor will provide a witness statement to confirm that the investigations have been carried out.

Produce written evidence of your investigation, including a list of equipment and apparatus used, an explanation of your method, clearly tabulated results and your calculations of the efficiency of each device.

From the results you obtained, show by calculation how efficient each device is in transforming energy from one type to another.

This provides evidence for P1 and P2

Task 2
For both practical investigations undertaken for Task 1, describe the energy transformations that have taken place, using either block or Sankey diagrams.

Comment on your findings in regard to the efficiency of the transformation process in both these investigations.

This provides evidence for M1

Task 3
Drawing on the results of your investigations, and other research, explain how energy losses due to energy transformations in the home or workplace can be minimised to reduce the impact on the environment. You should provide an explanation of how you may be able to increase the efficiency of devices, such as by reducing heat loss, and information about whether there are alternative devices available.

Present your work as an information leaflet for consumers in the home and the workplace, providing advice on how to reduce the overall environmental impact.

This provides evidence for D1

To tabulate your results means putting them into an appropriate table with clear headings and units.

To explain means to give logical reasons to support your views.

To describe means to give a clear, straightforward description that includes all the main points. This can include illustrations.

Include sources of information that you selected on the basis of their relevance to the assignment.

Sources of information

Books

Arnold B (ed.) – *GCSE Science for Edexcel: Science Student Book* (Collins Educational, 2006) ISBN 9780007214488

Bell C, Brodie D, Dawson B and Tiernan A – *GCSE Applied Science for Edexcel: Teacher Pack* (Folens, 2006) ISBN 9781843039747

Johnson K — *New Physics for You* (Nelson Thornes, 2006) ISBN 9780748797943

Nuffield Curriculum Centre – *Twenty First Century Science: GCSE Physics Textbook* (OUP, 2006) ISBN 9780199150519

Safeguards Committee — *Safeguards in the School Laboratory* (Association for Science Education, 2006) ISBN 9780863574085

Websites

Association for Science Education www.ase.org.uk

Energy Saving Trust www.energysavingtrust.org.uk/

GCSE Revision www.gcse.com/energy.htm

Institute of Physicists www.iop.org

Learning Schools www.learningschools.net

Practical Physics www.practicalphysics.org

School Science www.schoolscience.co.uk

Science Museum www.sciencemuseum.org.uk

Science Consortium www.scienceconsortium.co.uk

This brief has beeen verified as being fit for purpose			
Assessor	Mr A Thomas		
Signature	Andrew Thomas	Date	11 October 2010
Internal verifier	Ms J Davies		
Signature	Jill Davies	Date	11 October 2010

Sample learner work

To inform the assessor which parts of the assignment the work relates to, include titles that are based on the task and grading criteria. This part clearly relates to P1 and P2.

Ensure that the method is clearly presented in stages, explaining exactly how the investigation was carried out and adding appropriate health and safety information.

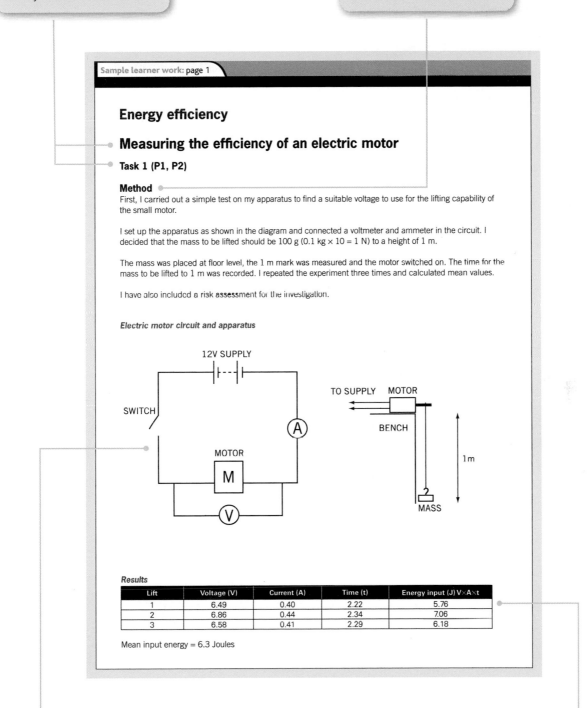

Sample learner work: page 1

Energy efficiency

Measuring the efficiency of an electric motor

Task 1 (P1, P2)

Method

First, I carried out a simple test on my apparatus to find a suitable voltage to use for the lifting capability of the small motor.

I set up the apparatus as shown in the diagram and connected a voltmeter and ammeter in the circuit. I decided that the mass to be lifted should be 100 g (0.1 kg × 10 = 1 N) to a height of 1 m.

The mass was placed at floor level, the 1 m mark was measured and the motor switched on. The time for the mass to be lifted to 1 m was recorded. I repeated the experiment three times and calculated mean values.

I have also included a risk assessment for the investigation.

Electric motor circuit and apparatus

12V SUPPLY

SWITCH

(A)

MOTOR

M

(V)

TO SUPPLY   MOTOR

BENCH

1 m

MASS

Results

Lift	Voltage (V)	Current (A)	Time (t)	Energy input (J) V×A×t
1	6.49	0.40	2.22	5.76
2	6.86	0.44	2.34	7.06
3	6.58	0.41	2.29	6.18

Mean input energy = 6.3 Joules

Illustrations should be well presented and include all relevant measurements and units. Here the learner has partially achieved P1.

The results should be clearly presented in a table and should include headings and units. Here the learner has partially achieved P2.

All formulae for calculations are present and laid out clearly for the assessor to grade. The learner has done the necessary work to partially achieve P2 for this investigation.

Where a new task and assessment criteria start, it is good practice to make this clear to the assessor to help them to grade your work.

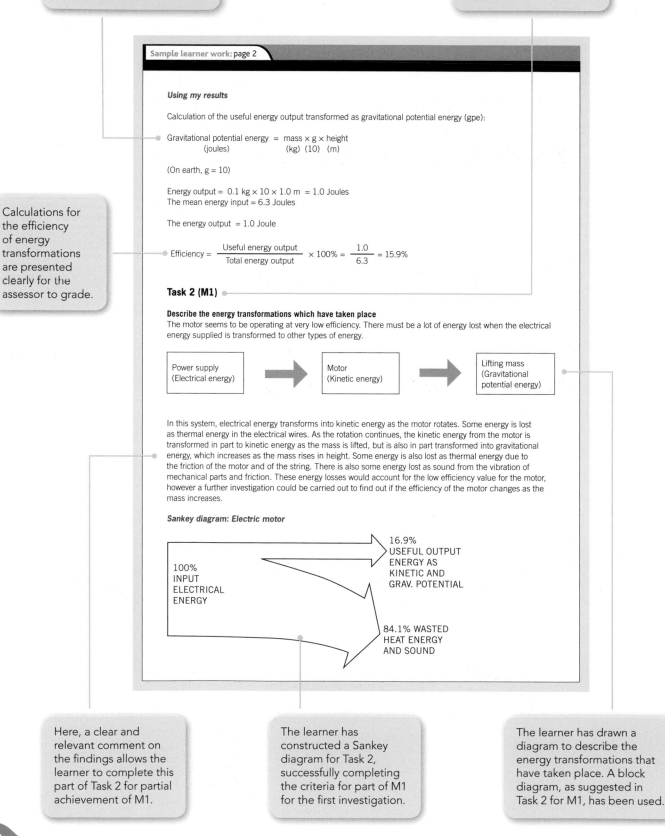

Sample learner work: page 2

Using my results

Calculation of the useful energy output transformed as gravitational potential energy (gpe):

Gravitational potential energy $=$ mass $\times$ g $\times$ height
(joules) (kg) (10) (m)

(On earth, g = 10)

Energy output = 0.1 kg $\times$ 10 $\times$ 1.0 m = 1.0 Joules
The mean energy input = 6.3 Joules

The energy output = 1.0 Joule

Efficiency $= \dfrac{\text{Useful energy output}}{\text{Total energy output}} \times 100\% = \dfrac{1.0}{6.3} = 15.9\%$

Task 2 (M1)

Describe the energy transformations which have taken place
The motor seems to be operating at very low efficiency. There must be a lot of energy lost when the electrical energy supplied is transformed to other types of energy.

Power supply (Electrical energy) → Motor (Kinetic energy) → Lifting mass (Gravitational potential energy)

In this system, electrical energy transforms into kinetic energy as the motor rotates. Some energy is lost as thermal energy in the electrical wires. As the rotation continues, the kinetic energy from the motor is transformed in part to kinetic energy as the mass is lifted, but is also in part transformed into gravitational energy, which increases as the mass rises in height. Some energy is also lost as thermal energy due to the friction of the motor and of the string. There is also some energy lost as sound from the vibration of mechanical parts and friction. These energy losses would account for the low efficiency value for the motor, however a further investigation could be carried out to find out if the efficiency of the motor changes as the mass increases.

Sankey diagram: Electric motor

100% INPUT ELECTRICAL ENERGY

16.9% USEFUL OUTPUT ENERGY AS KINETIC AND GRAV. POTENTIAL

84.1% WASTED HEAT ENERGY AND SOUND

Calculations for the efficiency of energy transformations are presented clearly for the assessor to grade.

Here, a clear and relevant comment on the findings allows the learner to complete this part of Task 2 for partial achievement of M1.

The learner has constructed a Sankey diagram for Task 2, successfully completing the criteria for part of M1 for the first investigation.

The learner has drawn a diagram to describe the energy transformations that have taken place. A block diagram, as suggested in Task 2 for M1, has been used.

It is good practice to perform each experiment three times in order to get a mean value, making the result more accurate and also helping to identify anomalous values.

Again the learner has included a clear title relating to the task and grading criteria, which is good practice.

The learner has again added a brief method, including the equipment used, how it was used and health and safety measures taken, to contribute towards achievement of P1.

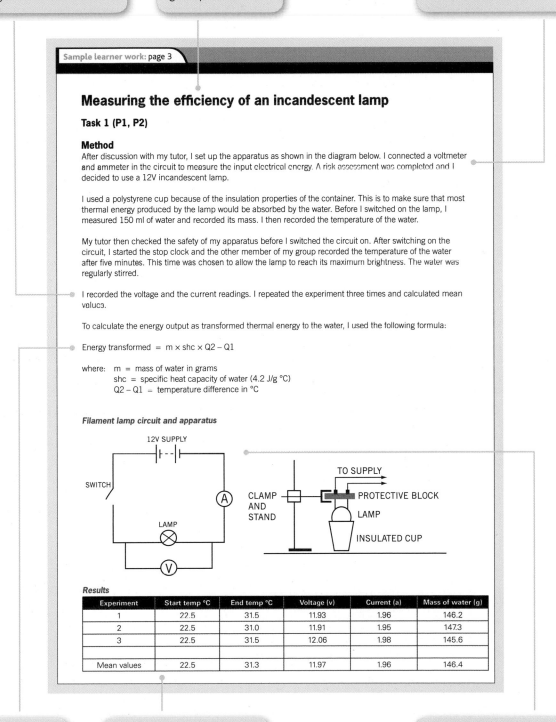

Sample learner work: page 3

Measuring the efficiency of an incandescent lamp

Task 1 (P1, P2)

Method

After discussion with my tutor, I set up the apparatus as shown in the diagram below. I connected a voltmeter and ammeter in the circuit to measure the input electrical energy. A risk assessment was completed and I decided to use a 12V incandescent lamp.

I used a polystyrene cup because of the insulation properties of the container. This is to make sure that most thermal energy produced by the lamp would be absorbed by the water. Before I switched on the lamp, I measured 150 ml of water and recorded its mass. I then recorded the temperature of the water.

My tutor then checked the safety of my apparatus before I switched the circuit on. After switching on the circuit, I started the stop clock and the other member of my group recorded the temperature of the water after five minutes. This time was chosen to allow the lamp to reach its maximum brightness. The water was regularly stirred.

I recorded the voltage and the current readings. I repeated the experiment three times and calculated mean values.

To calculate the energy output as transformed thermal energy to the water, I used the following formula:

Energy transformed $= m \times shc \times Q2 - Q1$

where: m = mass of water in grams
shc = specific heat capacity of water (4.2 J/g °C)
$Q2 - Q1$ = temperature difference in °C

Filament lamp circuit and apparatus

12V SUPPLY
SWITCH
A
LAMP
V
CLAMP AND STAND
TO SUPPLY
PROTECTIVE BLOCK
LAMP
INSULATED CUP

Results

Experiment	Start temp °C	End temp °C	Voltage (v)	Current (a)	Mass of water (g)
1	22.5	31.5	11.93	1.96	146.2
2	22.5	31.0	11.91	1.95	147.3
3	22.5	31.5	12.06	1.98	145.6
Mean values	22.5	31.3	11.97	1.96	146.4

Include any formulae you use in your calculations to help to inform the investigation.

A clear, well-presented table – including all headings and units and a row for the mean values – allows the learner to complete fully the requirements for P1.

Again the learner has included a clear, labelled diagram with all relevant measurements and units to demonstrate how the apparatus was set up, giving evidence towards P1.

The learner has set out how they have used the mean values to calculate the energy transformations and the percentage efficiency, fully meeting P2.

A block diagram has been used, along with a brief written paragraph, to describe the energy transformations that have taken place for further evidence towards M1 for the second investigation.

Sample learner work: page 4

Using my mean values

Mass of water	= 146.37g
Temp. difference	= 8.8°C
Voltage	= 11.97 V
Current	= 1.96 A
Time	= 300 s

Input energy: $= V \times A \times t$
$= 11.97 \times 1.96 \times 300 = 7038$ Joules

Energy transformed to heat: = mass x specific heat capacity × Q2 – Q1
$= 146.37 \times 4.2\ 8.8 = 5410$ Joules

I know that the energy transformed by the lamp to heat and light must total the energy supplied as electrical energy, from the law of conservation of energy and so:

Useful light energy produced:
(Electrical energy input – thermal energy output) = 7038 – 5410 = 1628 Joules

$$\text{Efficiency} = \frac{\text{Useful energy output}}{\text{Total energy output}} \times 100\% = \frac{1628J}{7038J} = 23\%$$

Task 2 (M1)

Describe the energy transformations which have taken place
The efficiency of the lamp is very low. Most of the electrical energy input is transformed to thermal energy, and since we really only need light from a lamp, most of our input electrical energy is wasted to the environment.

Power supply (Electrical energy)	→	Lamp (Heat + light)

In this system, electrical energy from the power supply is transformed directly into thermal energy as a result of the resistance of the filament to the flow of electrical current. As the filament gets hotter, some thermal energy is transformed to light but most is wasted and spreads out into the environment.

From my research I have discovered that higher power-rated incandescent lamps produce a lot more thermal energy and are much less efficient.

Sankey diagram: 12V Filamant Lamp

100% INPUT ELECTRICAL ENERGY

23% USEFUL OUTPUT ENERGY AS LIGHT

77% WASTED HEAT ENERGY

It is good practice to include a brief conclusion, confirming the evidence that the research has provided.

A further Sankey diagram for this investigation has been added to describe the energy transformations that have taken place. This successfully fulfils the requirements for achievement of criterion M1.

The learner has commented on the findings from the investigation, which provides further evidence for M1.

When recording your risk assessment for an investigation, include the unit number and title, the assignment title and the particular task.

Include a list of any classroom preparations made to avoid risk to the health and safety of yourself and others.

Hazards should be listed and must include any aspect of the investigation that could possibly cause harm or damage.

Sample learner work: page 5

Risk assessment for first experiment

Unit title	Unit 2: Energy and Our Universe
Assignment title	Energy efficiency
Task	Measuring the efficiency of an electric motor

Classroom preparation

Ensure all coats, bags and non-essential items are removed from the area.

Make available all equipment within easy reach.

Check for loose and overhanging electrical wires.

Hair must be tied back and loose clothing fastened.

Electrical supply must be checked by the tutor to ensure a safe and suitable voltage for this investigation.

Hazards

Electrical power supply

Masses

Electrical leads

String

Motor fastening

Risk

The electrical supply could provide an unsuitable voltage output, which could cause a shock or spark.

The string may break, dropping the mass onto a person's foot.

The electrical leads could become tangled.

The motor fastening to the bench may become loose, causing it to drop onto a person's foot.

Action to be taken to reduce risk

Have the supply checked by the tutor.

Ensure the string is not worn.

Stand aside the bench when carrying out the work.

Number of people potentially affected

Two per group

Disposal of waste

No waste materials produced

Learner name	David Foster		
Learner signature	David Foster	Date	20 November 2010

Include actions that you could take to prevent or reduce any risk, include the number of people that could be affected and set out how you will dispose safely of any waste.

Add your name, signature and the date to any risk assessments to make them valid.

List all potential risks and, based on the hazards you have identified previously, explain briefly why each is a potential risk.

When recording your risk assessment for an investigation, include the unit number and title, the assignment title and the particular task.

Classroom preparation for any investigation should be relevant and include measures taken to prevent any risks to health and safety.

Hazards should be listed and must include any aspect of the investigation that could possibly cause harm or damage.

Sample learner work: page 6

Risk assessment for second experiment

Unit title	Unit 2: Energy and Our Universe	
Assignment title	Energy efficiency	
Task	Measuring the efficiency of an incandescent lamp	

Classroom preparation

Ensure all coats, bags and non-essential items are removed from the area.

Set out the equipment in an orderly manner.

Ensure that the water does not come into contact with electricity at any time.

Check for loose and overhanging electrical wires.

Hair must be tied back and loose clothing fastened.

There must be sufficient space within which to work safely.

Hazards

Electrical power supply

Water

Electrical leads

Lamp

Clamp and stand

Risk

The water could into contact with the electrical supply, causing shock.

The electrical leads could become tangled around objects.

The lamp will become hot and could cause burns if touched.

The clamp stand could be knocked over, causing damage to equipment, or injury.

Action to be taken to reduce risk

Have the apparatus assembly checked by the tutor.

Make sure that the metal part of the lamp and the electrical contacts are not in contact with the water before switching on the circuit.

Take care when stirring the thermometer to avoid touching the lamp or causing too much water movement.

One person to be ready at the power supply switch at all times.

Number of people potentially affected

Two per group

Disposal of waste

No waste materials produced

Learner name	David Foster		
Learner signature	David Foster	Date	20 November 2010

Include actions that you could take to prevent or reduce any risk, include the number of people that could be affected and set out how you will dispose safely of any waste.

Add your name, signature and the date to any risk assessments to make them valid. This is a necessary part of the assessment criteria for P1.

List all potential risks and, based on the hazards you have identified previously, explain briefly why each is a potential risk.

A title page introducing Task 3 (D1) is used here. This model of good practice is used to identify the task requiring construction of an information leaflet.

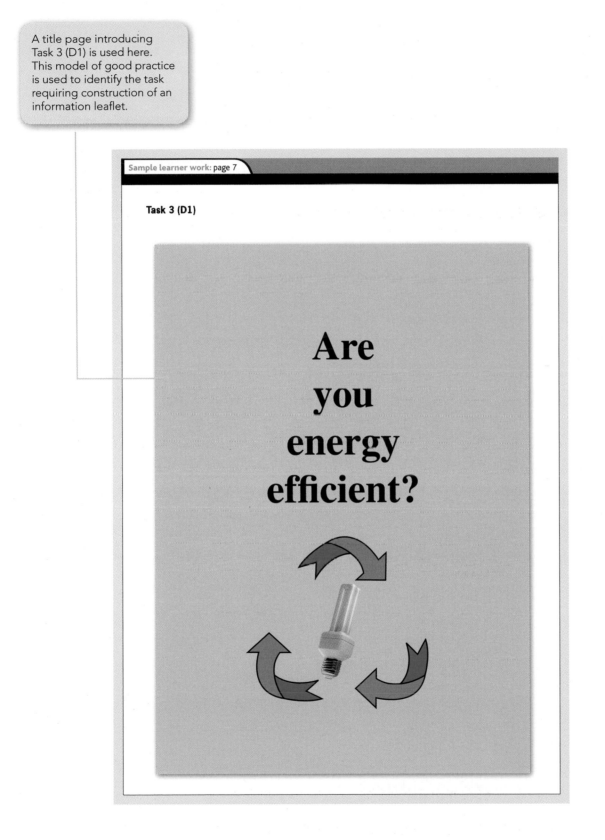

Sample learner work: page 7

Task 3 (D1)

Are you energy efficient?

Including a brief introduction to the overall task is a good way to start.

Use subtitles to break up the information, to put it in a relevant order and to check that you have included everything required for D1.

Sample learner work: page 8

In general, energy loss in all devices usually takes the form of heat (thermal) energy and sound. Unfortunately, when energy is transformed from one type to another, it is very difficult to reduce this 'wasted' energy and almost impossible to prevent energy loss completely.

Energy transformations

Our homes and workplaces are full of devices which transform energy. The majority transform electrical energy to a type of energy which we need. However, when electrical energy is transformed, most devices in use at the moment produce both useful output energy and an energy type which is difficult to use or cannot be used again. Heat and sound are termed waste energy for most devices, although sound energy makes up a much smaller percentage of the energy lost

Generally, in order to minimise energy losses in the home and workplace, we need to find ways of reducing wasted heat energy when electrical energy is transformed to other useful types.

What is the impact on the environment?

Electricity comes from a variety of sources because the electrical grid system is quite complex. We may be using electricity generated by gas, coal or nuclear power from power stations all over the UK, which is fed into the same supply grid. These power stations emit CO_2, radioactive waste and other harmful gases and materials into the environment, either directly into the atmosphere or to the ground and waterways.

The problems

- CO_2 levels in the atmosphere are a major concern. This gas prevents certain wavelengths of heat radiation from escaping from the surface of the earth back into space.
- A build-up of CO_2 will cause the average temperature to increase in the lower atmosphere. This is global warming. Over the last 50 years there has been a sustained increase in CO_2 levels caused in general by burning fossil fuels.
- Electricity-generating power stations burn significant amounts of fossil fuels. Unless we can replace these power stations by harnessing natural energy resources we must continue to make electricity in this way and find ways to reduce waste energy.
- The costs of producing electricity using most of the methods listed in the table below are much higher than in conventional power stations.

Research has provided supporting evidence to help towards successful completion of D1.

Bullet points are an excellent way of breaking up large amounts of text into smaller manageable chunks of relevant information.

Research has allowed the learner to collate lots of useful information for the comparison of different alternative energy sources.

A table is a good way of presenting information, such as the advantages and disadvantages of alternative energy sources.

Sample learner work: page 9

Alternative energy source	Description, and advantages and disadvantages
Hydro-electricity	Generated by falling water from a lake spinning a turbine. Clean and renewable form of energy. Dependent on rainfall and considered by some as unsightly. Fairly high power output can be produced (+5MW)
Wind	Natural winds spin turbine blades connected directly to the generator. Clean and renewable form of energy. High construction costs and maintenance. Visually spoil the countryside or coast, and winds are unpredictable. Low power output. (1kW – 3MW per turbine)
Geothermal	Water is heated by natural radioactive elements in the crust and is put through a heat exchanger to make steam which drives a turbine. Clean and renewable form of energy. High construction costs and suitable rocks are found in few areas. Fairly low power output (3-3.5 MW)
Wave	The up and down motion of the waves can be used to rotate the axle of a generator at sea. Clean and renewable. Costs to manufacture are high and maintenance is difficult. They would be visually damaging to the coastline if close to shore. Low power output depending on length (+1MW)
Tidal	Rise and fall of the tides can be contained using barrages and then released down shafts to drive turbines. Clean and renewable energy source. Very high costs needed to build the barrage and displaces natural wildlife. Fairly high power output (30MW – 9GW)
Solar	Conversion of sunlight directly to electrical energy by using photo-voltaic cells. Clean and renewable energy source. Costs are high initially. They are only useful in countries where long sunshine hours are guaranteed. Low power output (up to 0.5 MW)

A question is a good way of introducing another part of the information leaflet that relates directly to the reader.

What can we do?

There are a number of things we can do to help reduce the amount of energy wasted. This would result in a reduction of electricity used, lowering the demand for electricity and so reducing the amount of CO_2 and harmful products emitted into the environment:

- Use large appliances more efficiently. Use washing machines, dishwashers and tumble driers when fully loaded, since most washing cycles last the same amount of time.
- Use smaller appliances more efficiently. Kettles, microwaves, other kitchen appliances, lamps etc should be on only when necessary. Boil only sufficient water for your needs. Switch off lamps in rooms where light is not needed.
- Switch off the 'standby' modes. Electrical equipment which is maintained on standby, accounts for up to 15 per cent of annual household electrical costs. This equipment includes computers, TVs, satellite boxes, DVD players, alarm clocks, printers, cooker displays.
- Thermostatic valves. Make sure that all radiators in a home or workplace are fitted with good valves which regulate the heat more efficiently.
- Recycle water. Use water more than once if possible, for example, bath water can be used to water plants.
- Reduce your travel. Only travel in vehicles from home to work and other places if you cannot walk or cycle the route effectively. Share lifts if possible.
- Insulate. Homes and workplaces that are insulated well against heat loss do not need to have heating systems on high settings. By lowering the setting, less energy is used and, therefore, wasted. Insulation of 180 mm thickness reduces heat loss by 25 per cent.
- Install Home Energy meters. We can all regularly check our energy usage which helps us to change our attitude to using electricity.

This table shows the reduction in CO_2 emissions that can be achieved if old appliances are replaced with new ones in one home for the lifetime of the appliance.

Appliance	CO_2 (kg)
Dishwasher	85
Fridge/freezer	150
Washing machine	42
Tumble drier	251

A table is used here to show how energy can be saved in the home, reducing environmental impact.

Using shaded boxes to highlight important information is good practice, especially in information leaflets.

The use of illustrations, diagrams and photographs is also good practice – it makes the leaflet more interesting and breaks up text.

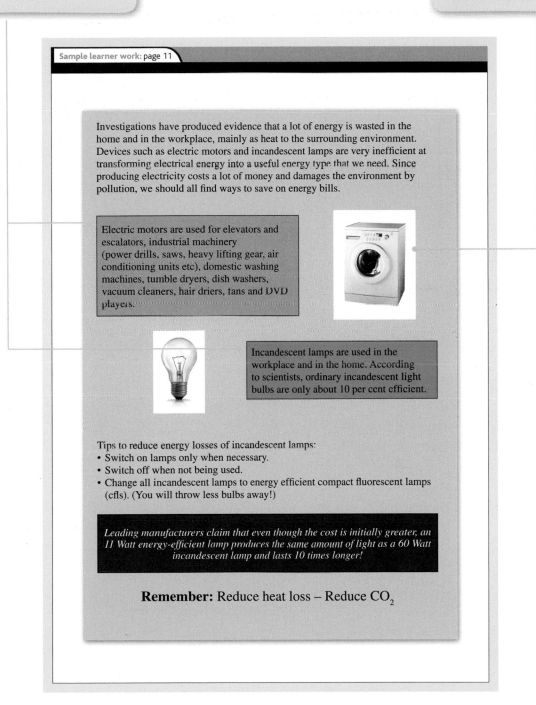

Sample learner work: page 11

Investigations have produced evidence that a lot of energy is wasted in the home and in the workplace, mainly as heat to the surrounding environment. Devices such as electric motors and incandescent lamps are very inefficient at transforming electrical energy into a useful energy type that we need. Since producing electricity costs a lot of money and damages the environment by pollution, we should all find ways to save on energy bills.

Electric motors are used for elevators and escalators, industrial machinery (power drills, saws, heavy lifting gear, air conditioning units etc), domestic washing machines, tumble dryers, dish washers, vacuum cleaners, hair driers, fans and DVD players.

Incandescent lamps are used in the workplace and in the home. According to scientists, ordinary incandescent light bulbs are only about 10 per cent efficient.

Tips to reduce energy losses of incandescent lamps:
• Switch on lamps only when necessary.
• Switch off when not being used.
• Change all incandescent lamps to energy efficient compact fluorescent lamps (cfls). (You will throw less bulbs away!)

Leading manufacturers claim that even though the cost is initially greater, an 11 Watt energy-efficient lamp produces the same amount of light as a 60 Watt incandescent lamp and lasts 10 times longer!

Remember: Reduce heat loss – Reduce CO_2

The learner has produced a clear reference list of the books and websites used for research in this assignment.

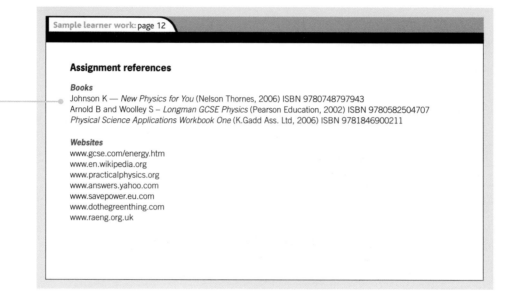

Sample learner work: page 12

Assignment references

Books
Johnson K — *New Physics for You* (Nelson Thornes, 2006) ISBN 9780748797943
Arnold B and Woolley S – *Longman GCSE Physics* (Pearson Education, 2002) ISBN 9780582504707
Physical Science Applications Workbook One (K.Gadd Ass. Ltd, 2006) ISBN 9781846900211

Websites
www.gcse.com/energy.htm
www.en.wikipedia.org
www.practicalphysics.org
www.answers.yahoo.com
www.savepower.eu.com
www.dothegreenthing.com
www.raeng.org.uk

Observation record of learner's work

Your tutor will complete an observation record while you are carrying out your investigation. You must hand this in with your assignment.

Learner name	David Foster
Programme	BTEC Level 2 First Certificate in Applied Science
Unit number and title	Unit 2: Energy and Our Universe

Description of activity undertaken (please be as specific as possible)

Learner to select and set up suitable apparatus for investigating efficiency of energy transformations in an electric motor and filament lamp

Learner to carry out activities using strict safety guidelines

Learner to record experiment results in standard format

Learner to perform essential calculations using primary data

Assessment and grading criteria

P1: Carry out practical investigations that demonstrate how various types of energy can be transformed.

P2: Calculate the efficiency of energy transformations.

How the activity meets the requirements of the assessment and grading criteria

The activity took place in the appropriate physics laboratory under the supervision of the assessor and senior technician.

The learner correctly chose instruments and equipment for investigation purposes for measurement of the efficiency of an electric motor and filament lamp.

Risk assessments were completed prior to the start of the practical activity. Laboratory safety guidelines were observed throughout the activities. Observations and relevant measurements were systematically carried out and recorded. There was evidence of preliminary set-up and good experimental practice. The experiments were repeated appropriately.

Calculations of energy input and energy output were made and efficiencies determined with minimal guidance.

Learner signature	David Foster	Date	20 November 2010
Assessor signature	Andrew Thomas	Date	20 November 2010
Assessor name	Mr A Thomas		

The observation record should be signed and dated by the learner in order to be valid.

Sample assessor's comments

It is valuable to reflect on your assignment work. This includes looking at things that you enjoyed and that went well, as well as areas that you found difficult.

The assessor will mark a Y (yes) or N (no) next to each of the grading criteria to show whether it has been achieved or not.

Qualification	BTEC Level 2 First Certificate in Applied Science	Year	2010–2011
Unit number and title	Unit 2: Energy and Our Universe	Learner name	David Foster

Grading criteria	Achieved?
P1 carry out practical investigations that demonstrate how various types of energy can be transformed	Y
P2 calculate the efficiency of energy transformations	Y
M1 describe the energy transformations and the efficiency of the transformation process in these investigations	Y
D1 explain how energy losses due to energy transformations in the home or workplace can be minimised to reduce the impact on the environment	Y

Learner feedback

I really enjoyed this assignment because I like doing practical investigations. The lesson taught me that some devices are more efficient than others and I know now how to save energy in my home. There were many things to consider in this investigation and I had to set up the apparatus a number of times before I was happy to begin recording. This practical needed two of us to record all the electrical figures and times.

Assessor feedback

A very neatly produced assignment with clear and well-documented investigative results. You have repeated your results, which is also very good practice. You have completed suitable risk assessments and shown a mature approach to your work. All aspects of practical set up and investigation have been carried out largely independently. Your calculations are clear and accurate, and to suitable significant figures for the purpose. Criteria P1 and P2 met.

Energy transformations for both devices have been explained. There are clear descriptions of the energy transformations at key stages in the operation of each device and Sankey diagrams. A valid comment of the efficiencies calculated for both devices is provided, with consideration of the possible reasons for low efficiency values.
Criterion M1 met.

You have linked the low efficiency values to areas of energy loss in each system and suggested valid ways in which these losses can be reduced. There is a good understanding of the science of energy transformation in your explanation and independent research has been used to help inform your decisions concerning ways of reducing energy losses in these devices in the home and workplace and how to reduce the overall environmental impact. Criterion D1 met.

Well done.

Action plan

Investigations like these sometimes produce a wide range of results. It would be a good idea to compare your methods with other groups to help you decide where improvements can be made.

Assessor signature	Andrew Thomas	Date	19 January 2011
Learner signature	David Foster	Date	19 January 2011

The action plan is very important because it tells you what you need to do in future assignments to improve your grade.

Coping with problems

Most learners sail through their BTEC First with no major problems. Unfortunately, not everyone is so lucky. Some may have personal difficulties or other issues that disrupt their work so they are late handing in their assignments. If this happens to you, it's vital to know what to do. This checklist should help.

Checklist for coping with problems

✔ Check that you know who to talk to.

✔ Don't sit on a problem and worry about it. Talk to someone promptly, in confidence. It's always easier to cope if you've shared it with someone.

✔ Most centres have professional counsellors you can talk to if you prefer. They won't repeat anything you say to them without your permission.

✔ If you've done something wrong or silly, people will respect you more if you are honest, admit where you went wrong and apologise promptly.

Case study: Dealing with problems

Sabena has lots of personal problems. Her grandmother in India is very ill and her mother has gone to help look after her. Sabena's father works long hours at the local factory, leaving Sabena to look after her three younger brothers. She is responsible for feeding the family, washing and ironing their clothes, and getting the boys to school.

Sabena finds this very difficult as she is currently in the middle of her BTEC First in Applied Science; she has lots of assignments to complete and the deadlines are getting nearer. She hasn't told anyone about her situation but feels that she can't cope any longer.

Sabina starts to fall behind with her assignments and fails to hand in two on time. Unaware of her situation, Sabena's tutor tells her off for missing the deadlines and decides to discipline her, which could lead to temporary exclusion or being asked to leave the course altogether. Sabena bursts into tears and the tutor takes her into a quiet room to talk. Sabena tells her everything, but doesn't want anyone else to know.

The tutor wishes Sabena had spoken to her earlier and suggests that she should make an appointment with the student counselling staff. Sabena does this and is surprised to find how much help is available. Sabina's counsellor arranges extensions on her assignments until her mother returns from India, and some one-to-one help at support workshops.

What would you do if you had a problem like Sabena? What could Sabena have done differently to help herself?

TOP TIP

If you have a serious complaint or concern, talk to your chosen tutor first – for example if you believe an assignment grade is unfair. All centres have official procedures to cover important issues such as appeals about assignments and formal complaints but it's usually sensible to try to resolve a problem informally first.

Activity: What to do if problems occur

1 Make a list of the people who you can talk to if you ever need help.

2 Who could you approach in your centre, if you ever have a problem, concern or complaint? This could be a problem at home or at college, perhaps to do with a disagreement on teaching methods or the marking of an assignment for example.

3 Find out the names of your centre's counselling staff and where the service is situated. Make a note of this below – you never know when you might need them.

4 If you have issues with language, basic reading and writing skills, dyslexia or another disability, your centre needs to know. Find out the names of your centre's learning support staff and where the service is situated. Make a note of this below.

5 If you ever did anything really silly which could affect your studies (for example, copying someone else's work, getting involved in a dispute with your peers, messing about outside college), what would you do?

   a) Keep it to myself and hope no one finds out.

   b) Admit it and face the consequences.

   c) Lie when confronted about the matter.

TOP TIP

Remember, honesty is the best policy and will get a problem sorted out quickly.

Skills building

To do your best in your assignments you need a number of skills, including:

- your **personal, learning and thinking skills**
- your **functional skills** of ICT, mathematics and English
- your proofreading and document production skills.

Personal, learning and thinking skills (PLTS)

These are the skills, personal qualities and behaviour that you find in people who are effective and confident at work. These people enjoy carrying out a wide range of tasks, always try to do their best and work well alone or with others. They enjoy a challenge and use new experiences to learn and develop.

Activity: How good are your PLTS?

1 Do this quiz to help you identify areas for improvement.

a) I get on well with other people.

Always **Usually** **Seldom** **Never**

b) I try to find out other people's suggestions for solving problems that puzzle me.

Always **Usually** **Seldom** **Never**

c) I plan carefully to make sure I meet my deadlines.

Always **Usually** **Seldom** **Never**

d) If someone is being difficult, I think carefully before making a response.

Always **Usually** **Seldom** **Never**

e) I don't mind sharing my possessions or my time.

Always **Usually** **Seldom** **Never**

f) I take account of other people's views and opinions.

Always **Usually** **Seldom** **Never**

g) I enjoy thinking of new ways of doing things.

Always **Usually** **Seldom** **Never**

h) I like creating new and different things.

Always **Usually** **Seldom** **Never**

i) I enjoy planning and finding ways of solving problems.

Always **Usually** **Seldom** **Never**

j) I enjoy getting feedback about my performance.

Always **Usually** **Seldom** **Never**

k) I try to learn from constructive criticism so that I know what to improve.

Always **Usually** **Seldom** **Never**

l) I enjoy new challenges.

Always **Usually** **Seldom** **Never**

m) I am even-tempered.

Always **Usually** **Seldom** **Never**

n) I am happy to make changes when necessary.

Always **Usually** **Seldom** **Never**

o) I like helping other people.

Always **Usually** **Seldom** **Never**

Score 3 points for each time you answered 'Always', 2 points for 'Usually', 1 point for 'Seldom' and 0 points for 'Never'. The higher your score, the higher your personal, learning and thinking skills.

2 How creative are you? Test yourself with this activity. Identify 50 different objects you could fit into a matchbox at the same time! As a start, three suitable items are a postage stamp, a grain of rice, a staple. Can you find 47 more?

BTEC FACT

Your BTEC First qualification is at Level 2. Qualifications in functional skills start at Entry level and continue to Level 2. (You don't need to achieve functional skills to gain any BTEC qualification and the evidence from a BTEC assignment can't be used towards the assessment of functional skills.)

Functional skills

Functional skills are the practical skills you need to function confidently, effectively and independently at work, when studying and in everyday life. They focus on the following areas:

- Information and Communications Technology (ICT)
- Maths
- English.

You may already be familiar with functional skills. Your BTEC First tutors will give you more information about how you will continue to develop these skills on your new course.

ICT skills

These will relate directly to how much 'hands-on' practice you have had on IT equipment. You may be an experienced IT user and using word processing, spreadsheet and presentation software may be second nature. Searching for information online may be something you do every day – in between downloading music, buying or selling on eBay and updating your Facebook profile!

Or you may prefer to avoid computer contact as much as possible. If so, there are two things you need to do.

1   Use every opportunity to improve your ICT skills so that you can start to live in the 21st century!

2   Make life easier by improving your basic proofreading and document preparation skills.

Proofreading and document preparation skills

Being able to produce well-displayed work quickly will make your life a lot easier. On any course there will be at least one unit that requires you to use good document preparation skills.

Tips to improve your document production skills
✔ If your keyboarding skills are poor, ask if there is a workshop you can join. Or your library or resource centre may have software you can use.
✔ Check that you know the format of documents you have to produce for assignments. It can help to have a 'model' version of each type in your folder for quick reference.
✔ Practise checking your work by reading word by word – and remember not to rely on spellcheckers (**see** page 55).

Activity: How good are your ICT skills?

1a)   Test your current ICT abilities by responding *honestly* to each of the following statements.

   i)   I can create a copy of my timetable using a word-processing or spreadsheet package.
   True   False

   ii)   I can devise and design a budget for myself for the next three months using a spreadsheet package.
   True   False

   iii) I can email a friend who has just got broadband to say how to minimise the danger of computer viruses, what a podcast is and also explain the restrictions on music downloads.
   True   False

   iv) I can use presentation software to prepare a presentation containing four or five slides on a topic of my choice.
   True   False

   v)   I can research online to compare the performance and prices of laptop computers and prepare an information sheet using word-processing software.
   True   False

   vi) I can prepare a poster, with graphics, for my mother's friend, who is starting her own business preparing children's party food, and attach it to an email to her for approval.
   True   False

TRY THIS

Learning to touch type can save you hours of time. To check your keyboarding skills go to www.pearsonhotlinks.co.uk, insert the express code 5797S and click on the link for this page.

TOP TIP

Print your work on good paper and keep it flat so that it looks good when you hand it in.

1b) Select any one of the above to which you answered false and learn how to do it.

2 Compare the two tables below. The first is an original document; the second is a typed copy. Are they identical? Highlight any differences you find and check them with the key on page 97.

Name	Date	Time	Room
Abbott	16 July	9.30 am	214
Grey	10 August	10.15 am	160
Johnston	12 August	2.20 pm	208
Waverley	18 July	3.15 pm	180
Jackson	30 September	11.15 am	209
Gregory	31 August	4.20 pm	320
Marshall	10 September	9.30 am	170
Bradley	16 September	2.20 pm	210

Name	Date	Time	Room
Abbott	26 July	9.30 am	214
Gray	10 August	10.15 am	160
Johnson	12 August	2.20 pm	208
Waverley	18 July	3.15 am	180
Jackson	31 September	11.15 am	209
Gregory	31 August	4.20 pm	320
Marshall	10 September	9.30 pm	170
Bradley	16 August	2.20 pm	201

Maths or numeracy skills

Four easy ways to improve your numeracy skills

1 Work out simple calculations in your head, like adding up the prices of items you are buying. Then check if you are correct when you pay for them.

2 Set yourself numeracy problems based on your everyday life. For example, if you are on a journey that takes 35 minutes and you leave home at 11.10am, what time will you arrive? If you are travelling at 40 miles an hour, how long will it take you to go 10 miles?

3 Treat yourself to a maths training program.

4 Check out online sites to improve your skills. Go to www. pearsonhotlinks.co.uk, insert the express code 5797S and click on the link for this page.

TOP TIP

Quickly test answers. For example, if fuel costs 85p a litre and someone is buying 15 litres, estimate this at £1 x 15 (£15) and the answer should be just below this. So if your answer came out at £140, you'd immediately know you'd done something wrong!

Activity: How good are your maths skills?

Answer as many of the following questions as you can in 15 minutes. Check your answers with the key on page 97.

1 a) 12 + 28 = ?

  i) 30   ii) 34   iii) 38   iv) 40   v) 48

  b) 49 ÷ 7 = ?

  i) 6   ii) 7   iii) 8   iv) 9   v) 10

  c) ½ + 1¼ = ?

  i) ¾   ii) 1½   iii) 1¾   iv) 2¼   v) 3

  d) 4 × 12 − 8 × ?

  i) 5   ii) 6   iii) 7   iv) 8   v) 9

  e) 16.5 + 25.25 − ? = 13.25

  i) 28.5   ii) 31.25 iii) 34.5 iv) 41.65 v) 44

2 a) You buy four items at £1.99, two at 98p and three at £1.75. You hand over a £20 note. How much change will you get? _____

  b) What fraction of one litre is 250 ml? _____

  c) What percentage of £50 is £2.50? _____

  d) A designer travelling on business can claim 38.2p a mile in expenses. How much is she owed if she travels 625 miles? _____

  e) You are flying to New York in December. New York is five hours behind British time and the flight lasts eight hours. If you leave at 11.15 am, what time will you arrive? _____

  f) For your trip to the United States you need American dollars. You find that the exchange rate is $1.5 dollars.

  i) How many dollars will you receive if you exchange £500? _____

  ii) Last year your friend visited New York when the exchange rate was $1.8. She also exchanged £500. Did she receive more dollars than you or fewer – and by how much? _____

  g) A security guard and his dog patrol the perimeter fence of a warehouse each evening. The building is 480 metres long and 300 metres wide and the fence is 80 metres out from the building on all sides. If the guard and his dog patrol the fence three times a night, how far will they walk? _____

English skills

Your English skills affect your ability to understand what you read, prepare a written document, say what you mean and understand other people. Even if you're doing a practical subject, there will always be times when you need to leave someone a note, tell them about a phone call, read or listen to instructions – or write a letter for a job application!

Six easy ways to improve your English skills

1. Read more. It increases the number of words you know and helps to make you familiar with correct spellings.

2. Look up words you don't understand in a dictionary and check their meaning. Then try to use them yourself to increase your vocabulary.

3. Do crosswords. These help to increase your vocabulary and practise your spelling at the same time.

4. You can use websites to help you get to grips with English vocabulary, grammar and punctuation. Go to www.pearsonhotlinks.co.uk, insert the express code 5797S and click on the link for this page.

5. Welcome opportunities to practise speaking in class, in discussion groups and during presentations – rather than avoiding them!

6. Test your ability to listen to someone else by seeing how much you can remember when they've finished speaking.

Activity: How good are your English skills?

1. In the table below are 'wrong' versions of words often spelled incorrectly. Write the correct spellings on the right. Check your list against the answers on page 97.

Incorrect spelling	Correct spelling
accomodation	
seperate	
definate	
payed	
desparate	
acceptible	
competant	
succesful	

2 Correct the error(s) in these sentences.

   a) The plug on the computer is lose.

   b) The car was stationery outside the house.

   c) Their going on they're holidays tomorrow.

   d) The principle of the college is John Smith.

   e) We are all going accept Tom.

3 Punctuate these sentences correctly.

   a) Toms train was late on Monday and Tuesday.

   b) She is going to France Belgium Spain and Italy in the summer.

   c) He comes from Leeds and says its great there.

4 Read the article on copyright.

Copyright

Anyone who uses a photocopier can break copyright law if they carry out unrestricted photocopying of certain documents. This is because The Copyright, Designs and Patents Act 1988 protects the creator of an original work against having it copied without permission.

Legally, every time anyone writes a book, composes a song, makes a film or creates any other type of artistic work, this work is treated as their property (or copyright). If anyone else wishes to make use of it, they must get permission to do so and, on occasions, pay a fee.

Licences can be obtained to allow educational establishments to photocopy limited numbers of some publications. In addition, copies of an original document can be made for certain specific purposes. These include research and private study. Under the Act, too, if an article is summarised and quoted by anyone, then the author and title of the original work must be acknowledged.

a) Test your ability to understand unfamiliar information by responding to the following statements with 'True' or 'False'.

i) Students and tutors in schools and colleges can copy anything they want.
True   False

ii) The law which covers copyright is The Copyright, Designs and Patents Act 1988.
True   False

iii) A student photocopying a document in the library must have a licence.
True   False

iv) Copyright only relates to books in the library.
True   False

v) If you quote a newspaper report in an assignment, you don't need to state the source.
True   False

vii) Anyone is allowed to photocopy a page of a book for research purposes.
True   False

b) Make a list of key points in the article, then write a brief summary in your own words.

5 Nikki has read a newspaper report that a horse racing in the Kentucky Derby had to be put down. The filly collapsed and the vet couldn't save her. Nikki says it's the third time in two years a racehorse has had to be put down in the US. As a horse lover she is convinced racing should be banned in Britain and the US. She argues that fox hunting was banned to protect foxes, and that racehorses are more important and more expensive than foxes. Darren disagrees. He says the law is not working, hardly anyone has been prosecuted and fox hunting is going on just like before. Debbie says that animals aren't important whilst there is famine in the world.

a) Do you think the three arguments are logical? See if you can spot the flaws and check your ideas with the suggestions on page 97.

b) Sporting activities and support for sporting teams often provoke strong opinions. For a sport or team of your choice, identify two opposing views that might be held. Then decide how you would give a balanced view. Test your ideas with a friend or family member.

Answers

Skills building answers

ICT activities

2 Differences between the two tables are highlighted in bold.

Name	Date	Time	Room
Abbott	**16** July	9.30 am	214
Grey	10 August	10.15 am	160
Johnston	12 August	2.20 pm	208
Waverley	18 July	3.15 **pm**	180
Jackson	**30** September	11.15 am	209
Gregory	31 August	4.20 pm	320
Marshall	10 September	9.30 **am**	170
Bradley	16 **September**	2.20 pm	**210**

Maths/numeracy activities

1 **a)** iv, **b)** ii, **c)** iii, **d)** ii, **e)** i

2 **a)** £4.83, **b)** ¼, **c)** 5%, **d)** £238.75, **e)** 2.15 pm, **f) i)** $750 **ii)** $150 dollars more, **g)** 6.6 km.

English activities

1 Spellings: accommodation, separate, definite, paid, desperate, acceptable, competent, successful

2 Errors:
a) The plug on the computer is <u>loose</u>.
b) The car was <u>stationary</u> outside the house.
c) <u>They're</u> going on <u>their</u> holidays tomorrow.
d) The <u>principal</u> of the college is John Smith.
e) We are all going <u>except</u> Tom.

3 Punctuation:
a) Tom's train was late on Monday and Tuesday.
b) She is going to France, Belgium, Spain and Italy in the summer.
c) He comes from Leeds and says it's great there.

4 **a) i)** False, **ii)** True, **iii)** False, **iv)** False, **v)** False, **vi)** False, **vii)** True

5 A logical argument would be that if racehorses are frequently injured in a particular race, eg one with difficult jumps, then it should not be held. It is not logical to compare racehorses with foxes. The value of the animal is irrelevant if you are assessing cruelty. Darren's argument is entirely different and unrelated to Nikki's. Whether or not fox hunting legislation is effective has no bearing on the danger (or otherwise) to racehorses. Finally, famine is a separate issue altogether. You cannot logically 'rank' problems in the world to find a top one and ignore the others until this is solved!

Accessing website links

Links to various websites are referred to throughout this BTEC Level 2 First Study Skills Guide. In order to ensure that these links are up-to-date, that they work and that the sites aren't inadvertently linked to any material that could be considered offensive, we have made the links available on our website: www.pearsonhotlinks.co.uk. When you visit the site, please enter the express code 5797S to gain access to the website links and information on how they can be used to help you with your studies.

Useful terms

Apprenticeships
Schemes that enable you to work and earn money at the same time as you gain further qualifications (an NVQ award and a technical certificate) and improve your functional skills. Apprentices learn work-based skills relevant to their job role and their chosen industry. Go to www.pearsonhotlinks.co.uk, insert the express code 5797S and click on the link for this useful term to find out more.

Assessment methods
Methods, such as practical tasks and assignments, which are used to check that your work demonstrates the learning and understanding you need to obtain the qualification.

Assessor
The tutor who marks or assesses your work.

Assignment
A complete task or mini-**project** set to meet specific grading criteria.

Assignment brief
The information and instructions related to a particular assignment.

BTEC Level 3 Nationals
Qualifications you can take when you have successfully achieved a Level 2 qualification, such as BTEC First. They are offered in a variety of subjects.

Credit value
The number of credits attached to your BTEC course. The credit value increases relative to the length of time you need to complete the course, from 15 credits for a BTEC Certificate, to 30 credits for a BTEC Extended Certificate and 60 credits for a BTEC Diploma.

Command word
The word in an assignment that tells you what you have to do to produce the type of answer that is required, eg 'list', 'describe', 'analyse'.

Educational Maintenance Award (EMA)
A means-tested award which provides eligible learners under 19, who are studying a full-time course at a centre, with a cash sum of money every week. Go to www.pearsonhotlinks.co.uk, insert the express code 5797S and click on the link for this useful term to find out more.

Functional skills
The practical skills that enable all learners to use and apply English, maths and ICT both at work and in their everyday lives. They aren't compulsory to achieve on the course, but are of great use to you.

Grade
The rating of pass, merit or distinction that is given to an assignment you have completed, which identifies the standard you have achieved.

Grading criteria
The standard you have to demonstrate to obtain a particular grade in the unit. In other words, what you have to prove you can do.

Grading grid
The table in each unit of your BTEC qualification specification that sets out the grading criteria.

Indicative reading
Recommended books, magazines, journals and websites whose content is both suitable and relevant to the unit.

Induction
A short programme of events at the start of a course or work placement designed to give you essential information and introduce you to other people so that you can settle in easily.

Internal verification
The quality checks carried out by nominated tutors at all centres to ensure that all assignments are at the right level and cover appropriate learning outcomes. The checks also ensure that all **assessors** are marking work consistently and to the same standards.

Learning outcomes
The learning and skills you must demonstrate to show that you have learned a unit effectively.

Levels of study

The depth, breadth and complexity of knowledge, understanding and skills required to achieve a qualification determines its level. Level 2 is equivalent to GCSE level (grades A* to C). Level 3 equates to GCE A-level. As you successfully achieve one level, you can progress on to the next. BTEC qualifications are offered at Entry Level, then Levels 1, 2, 3, 4, 5, 6 and 7.

Mandatory units

On a BTEC Level 2 First course, these are the compulsory units that all learners must complete to gain the qualification.

Optional units

Units on your course from which you may be able to make a choice. They help you specialise your skills, knowledge and understanding and may help progression into work or further education.

Personal, learning and thinking skills (PLTS)

The skills and qualities that improve your ability to work independently and be more effective and confident at work. Opportunities for developing these are a feature of all BTEC First courses. They aren't compulsory to achieve on the course, but are of great use to you.

Plagiarism

Copying someone else's work or work from any other sources (eg the internet) and passing it off as your own. It is strictly forbidden on all courses.

Portfolio

A collection of work compiled by a learner – for an **assessor** – usually as evidence of learning.

Project

A comprehensive piece of work which normally involves original research and planning and investigation either by an individual or a team. The outcome will vary depending on the type of project undertaken. For example, it may result in the organisation of a specific event, a demonstration of a skill, a presentation or a piece of writing.

Tutorial

An individual or small group meeting with your tutor at which you discuss the work you are currently doing and other more general course issues.

Unit content

Details about the topics covered by the unit and the knowledge and skills you need to complete it.

Work placement

Time spent on an employer's premises when you carry out work-based tasks as an employee and also learn about the enterprise to develop your skills and knowledge.

Work-related qualification

A qualification designed to help you to develop the knowledge and understanding you need for a particular area of work.